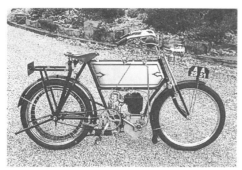
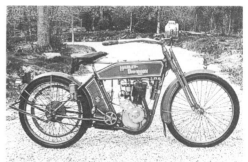

MILLER'S
Classic Motorcycles
PRICE GUIDE

MILLER'S CLASSIC MOTORCYCLES PRICE GUIDE 1997

Created and designed by
Miller's
The Cellars, High Street,
Tenterden, Kent, TN30 6BN
Tel: 01580 766411

Consultant: Judith Miller

General Editor: Mick Walker

Editorial and Production Co-ordinator: Sue Boyd
Editorial Assistants: Gillian Judd, Marion Rickman, Jo Wood
Production Assistants: Gillian Charles, Karen Taylor
Advertising Executive: Melinda Williams
Index compiled by: Hilary Bird
Design: Kari Reeves, Matthew Leppard, Shirley Reeves
Photographers: Ian Booth, Robin Saker

First published in Great Britain in 1996
by Miller's, an imprint of
Reed Consumer Books Limited,
Michelin House, 81 Fulham Road
London SW3 6RB
and Auckland, Melbourne, Singapore and Toronto

© 1996 Reed International Books Limited

A CIP catalogue record for this book is
available from the British Library

ISBN 1-85732-821-3

Illustrations by G. H. Graphics, St Leonard's-on Sea, E. Sussex.
Colour origination by Scantrans, Singapore
Printed and bound in England by William Clowes Ltd
Beccles and London

Miller's is a registered trademark of
Reed International Books Ltd

Front cover illustrations:

From top. 1954 BSA B33 500cc   *BKS*
Daily Mail Motorcycling Guide 1955   DM
1971 Laverda 750 Sportster   *BKS*
1925 Indian Big Chief 1204cc   *BKS*
A Honda Owners' Club of Great Britain Motorcycle Club Members' Badge   *CARS*
1953 BSA Bantam D1 123cc   *PS*

MILLER'S
Classic Motorcycles
PRICE GUIDE

Consultant
Judith Miller

General Editor
Mick Walker

1997
Volume IV

4

CONTENTS

ACKNOWLEDGEMENTS

Miller's Publications would like to acknowledge the great assistance given by our consultants.

Malcolm Barber   Tel: 01883 626553

Stuart Donovan   Mayfair Motors, PO Box No 66, Lymington, Hants
SO41 0XE Tel: 01590 644476

Brian Fox   Italian Vintage Company. Tel: 01673 842825

John Newson   Oxney Motorcycles, Rolvenden, Cranbrook, Kent TN17 4QA

John Sampson   Tel/Fax: 01769 550910

Brian Verrall   Woodlands, Mill Lane, Lower Beeding, Sussex RH13 6PX

We would like to extend our thanks to all auction houses and dealers who have assisted us in the production of this book.

KEY TO ILLUSTRATIONS

Each illustration and descriptive caption is accompanied by a letter code. By referring to the following list of Auctioneers (denoted by *) and Dealers (•) the source of any item may be immediately determined. Inclusion in this edition no way constitutes or implies a contract or binding offer on the part of any of our contributors to supply or sell the goods illustrated, or similar articles, at the prices stated. Advertisers in this year's directory are denoted by † and Motorcycle Clubs by §.

If you require a valuation for an item, it is advisable to check whether the dealer or specialist will carry out this service and if there is a charge. Please mention Miller's when making an enquiry. Having found a specialist who will carry out your valuation it is best to send a photograph and description of the item to the specialist together with a stamped addressed envelope for the reply. A valuation by telephone is not possible.

Most dealers are only too happy to help you with your enquiry, however, they are very busy people and consideration of the above points would be welcomed.

ADT   *   ADT Auctions Ltd, Classic & Historic Automobile Division, Blackbushe Airport, Blackwater, Camberley, Surrey, GU17 9LG Tel: 01252 878555

AOC   §   Ariel Owners Motor Cycle Club, Andy Hemingway, 80 Pasture Lane, Clayton, Bradford, Yorkshire, BD14 6LN

ARE   •   A.R.E. Ltd, East Street, Farnham, Surrey, GU9 7XU Tel: 01252 711777

AT   •   Andrew Tiernan, Vintage & Classic Motorcycles, Old Railway Station, Station Road, Framlingham, Nr Woodbridge, Suffolk, IP13 9EE Tel: 01728 724321

ATF   A. T. Fletcher, (Enthusiast & Collector).

AtMC   •†   Atlantic Motorcycles, 20 Station Road, Twyford, Berkshire, RG10 9NT Tel: 01734 342266

BKS   *†   Robert Brooks (Auctioneers) Ltd, 81 Westside, London, SW4 9AY Tel: 0171 228 8000

BLM   •†   Bill Little, Motorcycles, Oak Farm, Braydon, Swindon, Wiltshire, SN5 0AG Tel: 01666 860577

C   *   Christie, Manson & Woods Ltd, 8 King Street, St James's, London, SW1Y 6QT Tel: 0171 839 9060

CARS   •   C.A.R.S. (Classic Automobilia & Regalia Specialists), 4-4a Chapel Terrace Mews, Kemp Town, Brighton, Sussex, BN2 1HU Tel: 01273 601960

CBG   Classic Bike Guide, PO Box 28, Altrincham, Cheshire, WA15 8SH Tel: 0161 928 3480

CCR   •†   Charnwood Classic Restorations, 107 Central Road, Hugglescote, Coalville, Leicester, LE67 2FL Tel: 01530 832357

COYS   *   Coys of Kensington, 2-4 Queens Gate Mews, London, SW7 5QJ Tel: 0171 584 7444

CRC   †   Craven Collection of Classic Motorcycles, Brockfield Villa, Stockton-on-the-Forest, Yorkshire, YO3 9UE Tel: 01904 488461/400493

CRMC   §   Classic Racing Motorcycle Club, Membership Secretary, 3 Healey Avenue, High Wycombe, Bucks, HP13 7JP

CStC   •†   Cake Street Classics, Bellview, Cake Street, Laxfield, Nr Woodbridge, Suffolk, IP13 8EW Tel: 01986 798504

DB   •   David Baldock, North Road, Goudhurst, Kent, TN17 1AD Tel: 01580 211326

DM   •†   Don Mitchell & Company, 132 Saffron Road, Wigston, Leicestershire, LE18 4UP Tel: 0116 277 7669

DOT   §   Dot Owners Club, c/o Chris Black, 115 Lincoln Avenue, Clayton, Newcastle-upon-Tyne, Tyne & Wear, ST5 3AR

FMC   •   Faulkner & Son (Motorcycles) Ltd, 165-167 Botley Road, Oxford, Oxfordshire, OX2 0PB Tel: 01865 250147

GAZ   *   Thomas W. M. Gaze & Son, 10 Market Hill, Diss, Norfolk, IP22 3JZ Tel: 01379 651931

GLC   •   Greenlooms Classics, Greenlooms Farm, Hargrave, Chester, Cheshire, CH3 7RX Tel: 01829 781636

GRA   §   Greeves Riders Association, Dave & Brenda McGregor 4 Longshaw Close, North Wingfield, Chesterfield, Staffordshire, S42 5QR Tel: 01246 853846

HAG   •†   L. W. Haggis, 4 Peterhouse Parade, Graftens Drive, Pound Hill, Crawley, Sussex, RH10 3BA Tel: 01293 886451

HCH   *   Hobbs & Chambers, 15 Royal Crescent, Cheltenham, Glos, GL50 3DA Tel: 01242 513722

HH   •†   Hughie Hancox Restorations, R/O Obriens Buildings, 203-269 Foleshill Road, Coventry, West Midlands, CV1 4JZ Tel: 01203 552305

HOLL   *   Dreweatt Neate Holloways, 49 Parsons Street, Banbury, Oxfordshire, OX16 8PF Tel: 01295 253197

IMC   §   Indian Motorcycle Club, c/o John Chatterton (Membership secretary), 183 Buxton Road, Newtown, New Mills, Stockport, Cheshire, SK12 3LA Tel: 01663 747106

IMO   §   Italian Motorcycle Owners Club, c/o Rosie Marston (Membership Sec) 14 Rufford Close, Barton Seagrove, Kettering, Northants, NN15 6RF

IVC   •   The Italian Vintage Company, Tel: 01673 842825

JCZ   §   Jawa-CZ Owners Club, John Blackburn 39 Bignor Road, Sheffield, Yorkshire, S6 IJD

JIB   •   Jim Blanchard, 40 Cyrano Way, Grimsby, Humberside, DN37 9SQ Tel: 01472 885662

LDM   §   London Douglas Motorcycle Club, c/o Reg Holmes (Membership secretary), 48 Standish Avenue, Stoke Lodge, Patchway, Bristol, Avon, BS12 6AG

LEV   §   LE Velo Club Ltd, Kevin Parsons Chapel Mead, Blandford Hill, Winterbourne, Whitechurch, Blandford, Dorset, DT11 0AB

MAY   •†   Mayfair Motors, PO Box 66, Lymington, Hampshire, SO41 0XE Tel: 01590 644476

MOC   §   Maico Owners Club, c/o Phil Hingston, 'No Elms', Goosey, Faringdon, Oxfordshire, SN7 8PA Tel: 01367 710408

MR   *†   Martyn Rowe, Truro Auction Centre, Calenick Street, Truro, Cornwall, TR1 2SG Tel: 01872 260020

MWM   •   Wheeler Motorcycles Ltd, Mike, 108-110 High Street, Witney, Oxfordshire, OX8 6HT Tel: 01993 702660

NLM   •†   North Leicester Motorcycles, Whitehill Road, Ellistown, Leicestershire, LE67 1EL Tel: 01530 263381

OxM   •   Oxney Motorcycles, Rolvenden, Cranbrook, Kent, TN17 4NP Tel: 01797 270119

PC   Private Collection

PM   •†   Pollard's Motorcycles, The Garage, Clarence Street, Dinnington, Sheffield, Yorkshire, S31 7NA Tel: 01909 563310

PS   *†   Palmer Snell, 65 Cheap Street, Sherbourne, Dorset, DT9 3BA Tel: 01935 812218

PVE   §   Preston Vintage Enthusiasts

REC   §   Rudge Enthusiasts Club, c/o Colin Kirkwood, 41 Rectory Green, Beckenham, Kent, BR3 4HX Tel: 0181 658 0494

REOC   §   Royal Enfield Owners Club, c/o John Cherry, Meadow Lodge Farm, Henfield, Coalpit Heath, Avon, BS17 2UX

Rod   •   Rod Organ, (Sporting Images), 16 Coleville Avenue, Fawley, Southampton, Hampshire, SO45 1DA Tel: 01703 897958

ROY   •   Roy Barrett, 'Thatches', Southerton, Near Ottery St Mary, Devon, EX11 1SD Tel: 01395 568697

S   *   Sotheby's, 34-35 New Bond Street, London, W1A 2AA Tel: 0171 493 8080

SOF   §   Sunbeam Owners Fellowship, PO Box 7, Market Harborough, Leicestershire

SW   •   Spinning Wheel Garage, Sheffield Road, Sheepbridge, Chesterfield, Derbyshire, S41 9EH Tel: 01246 451772

TOC   §   Triumph Owners Club, c/o Mrs M. Mellish, 4 Douglas Avenue, Harold Wood, Romford, Essex, RM3 0UT

Vel   §   Velocette Owners Club, c/o David Allcock, 3 Beverley Drive, Trinity Fields, Stafford, Staffordshire, ST16 1RR

VER   •†   Brian R.Verrall, Woodlands, Mill Lane, Lower Beeding, Sussex, RH13 6PX Tel: 01403 891892

VMCC   §†   Vintage Motor Cycle Club, Allen House, Wetmore Road, Burton-on-Trent, Staffordshire, DE14 1TR Tel: 01283 540557

HOW TO USE THIS BOOK

Miller's Classic Motorcycles Price Guide presents an overview of the classic motorcycle marketplace during the past twelve months. In order to give you a comprehensive feel for what is available, we have included illustrations from a wide range of auction houses, dealers, motorcycle clubs and private individuals.

Following Miller's format, motorcycles are presented alphabetically by marque and chronologically within each group. Sidecars, specials, mopeds and scooters are dealt with in the same way at the end of the book. In the motorcycle memorabilia section, objects are grouped alphabetically by type, for example signs and petrol pumps, and then, where possible, chronologically within each grouping. Each illustration is fully captioned and carries a price range which reflects the dealer's or auctioneer's sale price. The prefix 'Est.' indicates the estimated price for the motorcycles which remained unsold at auction. Each illustration also carries an identification code which enables the reader to locate its source in the 'Key to Illustrations'.

We do not illustrate every classic motorcycle ever produced. Our aim is to reflect the marketplace, so if, for example, there appears to be a large number of Triumphs and only a few Vincents, this is a reflection of the quantity, availability and, to an extent, the desirability of these motorcycles in the marketplace over the last twelve months. If the motorcycle you are looking for is not featured under its alphabetical listing, do look in the colour sections and double-check the comprehensive index at the back of the book. If a particular motorcycle is not featured this year, it may well have appeared in previous editions of *Miller's Classic Motorcycle Price Guide,* which provides a growing visual reference library.

Please remember Miller's pricing policy: we provide you with a price GUIDE and not a price LIST. Our price ranges, worked out by a team of trade and auction house experts, reflect variables such as condition, location, desirability, and so on. Don't forget that if you are selling, it is possible that you will be offered less than the price range.

Lastly, we are always keen to improve the content and accuracy of our guides. If you feel that a particular make or model or other aspect of classic motorcycles has not been covered in sufficient detail, or if you have any other comments you would like to share with us about our book, please write and let us know. We value feedback from the people who use this guide to tell us how we can make it even better for them.

RESTORING A MOTORCYCLE TO CONCOURS CONDITION

The French term, *Concours d'Elégance*, refers to the judging of restored motorcycles and cars on the quality of overall appearance, the authenticity of accessories, the accuracy of specification and the techniques used for restoration. The 'Conkers' has in recent years become increasingly popular and, whilst not an exclusively English phenomenon, it is undoubtedly well and truly established here within the motorcycle world. By its nature, the Concours transcends all barriers since the quest for excellence is open to all. Some of the finest restorations have not emerged from professional workshops but from the kitchen table and the garden shed.

At a recent Brooks auction at the National Motorcycle Museum, there were machines dating from 1905–85 requiring restoration. Similar examples never fail to turn up at large sales and the machine you choose can be of any age and capacity. It is up to you to decide your budget and then buy from a reputable source. Be aware of the rarity of the bike before embarking.

Having found your project, the next step is to research the machine. Most popular makes are covered by marque clubs, and the Vintage Motorcycle Club with its specialist library and access to knowledgeable experts will provide invaluable help. Likewise, the motorcycle magazines can cater for most marques and there are also specialist bookshops which may help.

Probably the most trying problem, however, will be finding parts which, depending on the age and marque of the machine, can be hard to locate. A visit to the Motorcycle Show in Stafford, which takes place each April, will certainly open several avenues here, since many restorers are represented as well as useful expert contacts. The watchword is always patience.

Having assembled the machine from spares, finish is the next most important aspect but need not be too expensive. While it may be unwise to use powder coating when finishing the machine as it does not give the necessary gloss, stove enamel, which is very costly, is prone to chipping. The best choice for home restorers may be modern spray finishes. Properly used, the results can be impressive.

Finally the machine must be plated. Earlier machines generally require a dull nickel finish for authenticity although most now use polished nickel regardless and nickel is a much easier option for the home restorer as there are several kits available. For post-1928 machines, chrome plating is more appropriate but alas is harder to apply and nearly always requires professional attention.

Despite the effort required, it is important not to be put off restoring a bike to Concours condition. Most work can be carried out at home with perhaps larger jobs undertaken by reliable experts. It is patience and dedication which will see any enthusiast through.

FOREWORD

My first motorcycle race came about as a fourteen-year-old when my father seconded me into being his sidecar passenger. We actually won the event but were disqualified because of my age. My first solo win came at seventeen, at the little circuit that runs through Aberdare Park in Wales. I was riding a Vincent 500cc motorcycle which I had built whilst serving my apprenticeship at the Vincent Company in Stevenage.

My motorcycle racing career brought me British Championships and seven World Championships and, together with the motorcycle business which I opened in 1958, I have had the opportunity of riding both the most exotic race machines in the world and the most basic. On the occasions that I ride these days (which this year has taken me as far afield as New Zealand) I have been able to ride such wondrous machines as the Hailwood Hondas, the Moto Guzzi V8, the Benelli 4s and the Kompressor BMW etc, and for a short while I turn the clock back and relive the wonderful relationship with a superb piece of machinery which has been so satisfying.

The enthusiasts I encounter throughout my travels and their search for information never cease to amaze me. I am horrified at times when I see on the back of this enthusiasm some of the very misleading articles and material that are produced. I would therefore offer this advice if you are about to become a collector, restorer or are just in search of knowledge, pay attention. One way of doing this is through books such as *Miller's Classic Motorcycles Price Guide,* where the pictures alone act as a valuable guide. With this, and possibly some copies of original literature for the marque of your choice, you have a good basis on which to proceed and make your purchase or carry out your own restoration.

THE MOTORCYCLE MARKET

The International Classic Bike Show contract passed to Brooks this year, a decision which the Show organisers will no doubt feel was vindicated by the excellent result. Stafford in April tends to be judged as the barometer of the classic bike market, therefore, most of the pundits are saying that the market now sees prices a good deal healthier than they were a year ago. To an extent that is true, and there is firm evidence that the 'feel good factor' has permeated through to the motorcycle market. The admission of Finland and Austria into the EC has also brought new customers from these countries to the sales.

The market continues to become increasingly global, with recent sales witnessing personal appearances of bidders from the USA, the whole of Europe, and even Japan, whose bidders have preferred the telephone and fax in the past. Germans, doubtless with a thought to that country's wealth tax, are still notoriously shy at bidding in public, however, and unless legislation changes, they are likely to remain so. If any trend is becoming particularly noticeable it is that the less useable, less practical machines – particularly low capacity bikes of the '20s and earlier, the 'flat tankers' – are now less sought-after than was previously the case, and the same applies to very expensive Japanese racing machines which have limited application for Mr Everyman. Sadly, there are a great many of them.

Older machines with racing and competition provenance, particularly where this involves well-known and documented personalities, continue to attract a premium, and this was underlined at the Brooks Stafford sale in April when a 1924 Sunbeam Sprint Special achieved £16,445. It had originally competed at Brooklands and two prominent Brooklands exponents' names appeared in the log book. Folk heroes also tend to attract much attention, and thus it was that the ex-George Formby Norton International made about three times the normal price for the model at £14,950.

Large capacity machines of a sporting nature are still much sought-after, regardless of age, and the King Tut's tomb element also generates excitement. When both are combined, as in the case of the 'barn discovery' 1929 Coventry-Eagle Flying Eight at Stafford (a machine akin to a Brough Superior SS 100 in specification, and a good deal more rare) then £28,750 on the hammer was always on the cards, despite a top pre-sale estimate of only half this figure.

Quality, wherever it is found, still commands the best prices, whether the machine is restored or unrestored, but the same dictate cannot be applied to lesser machinery. The cost of restoring a cheap machine is very much the same as restoring an expensive one, and unless bidders have the skills and inclination to do the work themselves, they will avoid buying a 'grey porridge' type machine needing a lot of work unless it can be bought at rock-bottom prices.

Inevitably, and as the years pass, the ratio of British bikes to those of Japanese origin appearing at auction is altering in favour of the Japanese machines, and some excellent restorations of the Japanese classics are beginning to appear in ever greater numbers. This trend will inevitably continue, since most of the large British makers ceased production years ago, or are still producing only at token levels, and younger enthusiasts tend to identify with the machines with which they have grown up.

Significantly, there have been more dealers present at sales this year, and they have been bidding actively too, which is a sure sign that retail sales are improving. This contrasts with the classic car market, where retail selling is still relatively quiet outside the auction world. It seems unlikely that there will be more motorcycle sales this year than last, but the major auction houses holding them have changed their respective positions in the success stakes.

British bikes continue to be by far the most popular of the collectors' machines, but the ratio is altering year by year. Bike collectors continue to be generally more knowledgeable than their car contemporaries, with far more of them still carrying out their own restorations, and this ensures that sought-after spare parts sold at auction generally have a more enthusiastic reception than car parts sold in car sales. Machines in the £1,800–3,500 price bracket continue to account for the majority of sales.

Early Pioneer machines still sell for around £5,000–7,000, a situation which has not altered for some years, but European-built racing machinery has fared better than Japanese. On the 9th December 1995, Sotheby's achieved three good prices for Italian racing bikes – £20,000 for a 1952 MV Agusta Bialbero ex-works racer, £13,000 for a 1954 MV Augusta Monoalbero racer and £15,500 for a 1973 MV Agusta 750S of the type ridden by Mike Hailwood.

To sum up, the motorcycle market is healthy worldwide, and covers a broad spectrum of interest. It is less susceptible to hiccups in the world economy and is catered for far less in auction sales than the car market, although most of these have more lots on offer. It is now dominated by Brooks, Sotheby's and Palmer Snell, with few other companies seeking a share in this growing area.

Malcolm Barber
Managing Director – Brooks Auctioneers Ltd

ABC *(British 1913–22)*

1922 ABC 398cc Sports, transversely-mounted unit construction overhead valve engine, cylinders machined from steel billets, aluminium pistons, transmission comprises a car-type clutch, 4 speed gearbox, chain drive, cradle-type frame was notable for employing leaf-sprung suspension at both ends, restored.
£3,500–3,750 *BKS*

The ABC was not a commercial success, with a little over 3,000 being produced before assembly ceased in 1922.

1920 ABC overhead valve horizontally-opposed twin cylinder model 398cc, restored to original specification, little used since.
£3,250–3,750 *PS*

Designed by Granville Bradshaw and made by the All British (Engine) Company in the Sopwith Aircraft Company's premises.

ABINGDON *(British 1903–25)*

1920s Abingdon King Dick 89 Single Cylinder Overhead Valve 174cc, recently fully restored to very high standard, copy of original registration book and number, V5 log.
£2,500–2,750 *PS*

AERMACCHI *(Italian 1950–78)*

1957 Aermacchi Chimera 172.4cc.
£2,500–3,000 *PC*

First of the horizontal pushrod Aermacchi models, the futuristic Chimera (Dream) was launched at the Milan Show in November 1956.

1962 Aermacchi Ala d'Oro 246cc, original long-stroke engine, 4-speed gearbox, small Oldani brakes, lightweight forks.
£5,000–5,500 *PC*

1963 Aermacchi Ala d'Oro Racer 248cc, overhead valve, works-type machine with 5-speed engine, large Oldani front brake.
£4,000–4,250 *BKS*

r. **1965 Aermacchi Harley-Davidson 250cc,** 5-speed gearbox, very fast reliable motorcycle.
£2,000–2,500 *IVC*

1968 Aermacchi Ala d'Oro Racer 344cc,
overhead valve, Ceriani forks, 4LS front brake,
'N' camshaft.
£7,000–8,000 *PC*

1971 Aermacchi Sprint 344cc, overhead valve
horizontal single, 4 speed gearbox.
£900–1,500 *IVC*

1972 Aermacchi 350TV 344cc,
overhead valve engine.
£2,000–2,500 *IVC*

1973 Aermacchi Harley-Davidson SS350 344cc,
requires restoration, late model with full loop frame,
left-hand gear change, electric start.
£325–375 *MAY*

AJS *(British 1909–66)*
The 7R 'Boy Racer' Profile

When AMC's sales supremo and ex-racer, Jock West, aired the 7R AJS racer for the very first time at Brands Hatch (when it was still a grass track) in February 1948, it launched the career of possibly the premier British over-the-counter racer of the post-war period. Known as the 'Boy Racer', the Ajay featured a 348cc single overhead camshaft engine with a bore and stroke of 74 x 81mm. Full use was made of light alloys. The crankcase, a magnesium-alloy casting, was freely webbed, especially on the drive side where three rows of caged roller bearings supported the mainshaft. Although given the pre-war designation of 7R, the new machine shared nothing with its forebear, except for its capacity and the use of a single overhead camshaft driven by a Weller-tensioned chain.

The frame of the 7R was virtually a copy of the factory E90 Porcupine twin, a robust wide-spaced double cradle affair of welded steel tube. Modified AMC teledraulic forks,

oil-damped rear shocks and swinging arm looked after the suspension. Even the conical hubs with 2LS front and rear brakes all resembled the E90. Other technical details included a heavily finned light alloy cylinder barrel with a pressed-in iron liner, light alloy cylinder head, hairpin valve springs, a Lucas racing magneto, an Amal racing carburetter, and a separate Burman close-ratio gearbox.

A comprehensive pre-launch test programme ensured that machines were remarkably trouble free right from the start. As a result no fewer than 23 examples were entered for the Junior TT that year. Against stiff opposition privateer Maurice Cann brought his 7R home to a very creditable 5th position in the race.

The 7Rs scored countless race track successes even after production ceased in 1962. Many famous names were associated with these victories, such as Mike Hailwood, Bob McIntyre, Alan Shepherd, Les Graham, and many more.

1920 AJS 5/6hp V-Twin 748cc,
original instruction manuals, complete
and original, needs restoration.
£4,250–4,750 *BKS*

1926 AJS Big Port 500cc.
£6,250–6,750 *PM*

1928 AJS 348cc, restored, old style log book, Swansea V5.
£3,000–3,500 *BKS*
This example was once part of the Gangbridge Collection.

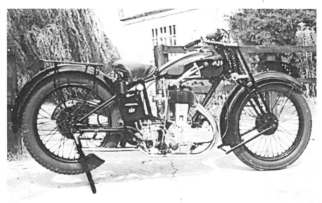

1929 AJS Model 9 500cc.
£2,500–3,000 *BLM*

1931 AJS Single Cylinder Twin Port R6 350cc, hand gear change, overhead valve.
£2,000–3,000 *CRC*

1931 AJS Model S1 V-Twin 998cc, big twin side valve, quick detachable and interchangeable wheels, 3-speed hand change gearbox, cork inset clutch, chain final drive, girder forks, coil spring front suspension, rigid frame at rear, original example.
£2,400–2,600 *BKS*

1936 AJS Model 26 347cc, electric lighting, single sprung dual seat, 3-speed gearbox, twin exhausts, chrome tank, black finish, correct specification, fully restored to very high standard.
Est. £3,600–3,800 *BKS*

1946 AJS Model 16M 348cc, overhead valve single, pillion pad, all black finish.
£1,500–2,000 *BLM*

1946 AJS 16M 348cc, overhead valve, base model of 69 x 93mm single with rigid frame and painted wheel rims.
£1,100–1,300 *MAY*

1946 AJS 16M 350cc, with de luxe passenger spring seat, otherwise original.
£1,400–1,600 *BKS*

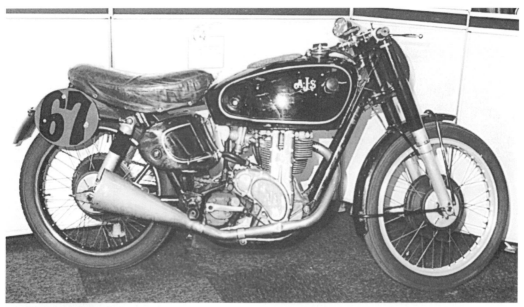

1948 AJS 7R 350cc.
£10,000–12,000 *VMCC*

This is one of the very first of the famous 7R 'Boy Racers' to be built. Original in virtually every respect, except rear wheel rim.

1950s AJS Model 16 Replica Trials Bike 350cc, replacement frame and gearbox, good restored condition, built for competition, no V5.
£1,400–1,600 *BKS*

This bike was ridden by Gordon Jackson at Chapleton Barton in 1988.

1952 AJS Model 20 498cc, overhead twin, non-standard mudguards, handlebars and saddle.
£1,400–1,600 *PS*

1951 AJS 18S 498cc,
overhead valve single.
£2,700–2,900 *BKS*

1953 AJS Model 18S 498cc.
£1,800–2,000 *BLM*

l. **1953 AJS Model 18CS Trials Bike 497cc,** light alloy barrel, increased ground clearance, smaller petrol tank, alloy mudguards, imported from US, AJS traditional black and gold livery, excellent condition, retains its distinctive 'Jampot' rear shock absorbers.
Est. £2,500–2,800 *S*

1953 AJS 16MS 348cc, rebuilt, paintwork very good, MOT.
Est. £1,400–1,600 *BKS*

l. **1953 AJS Model 20 500cc,**
twin cylinder.
£1,750–2,500 *CRC*

1955 AJS 16MS Trials Bike 347cc,
overhead valve, completely rebuilt.
Est. £2,000–2,500 *BKS*

Plumstead produced both Matchless and AJS trials and scramble models and fielded works teams in both areas with many independent riders also raising the reputation for the machines to well deserved heights.

1956 AJS Model 30 593cc, engine in running order, fitted with a period Avonaire fairing, good original condition throughout.
Est. £2,000–2,500 *S*

1957 AJS Model 16MS 348cc.
£1,500–2,000 *BLM*

1957 AJS Model 16M 348cc.
£1,500–2,000 *BLM*
This is one of the last models with forward mounted magneto.

> ## Don't Forget!
> *If in doubt please refer to the 'How to Use' section at the beginning of this book.*

l. **1958 AJS Model G9 498cc,** twin engine, related to a 1957 Matchless unit, Swansea V5.
£1,800–2,000 *BKS*

1958 AJS G9 498cc,
overhead valve twin.
Est. £2,000–2,200 *BKS*

1958 AJS 16MS 348cc, 69 x 93mm
bore and stroke, very good condition,
excellent runner.
£2,000–2,200 *BKS*

1960 AJS Model 8 348cc, overhead
valve single unit construction, larger
version of 248cc model, restored.
£700–800 *BKS*

1958 AJS 16MS 348cc.
£2,200–2,400 *BLM*
*The 1958 16MS differed from earlier models thanks to not
having the front mounted magneto.*

1959 AJS Model 18S 497cc, original example.
£2,250–2,650 *BLM*

1960 AJS Model 31 646cc, twin cylinder.
£2,000–3,000 *CRC*

1959 AJS Model 31 646cc.
£2,250–2,750 *BLM*
*The 31 with its 646cc engine replaced
the 593cc Model 30 at the end of 1958.*

**1961 AJS 7R Racing Motorcycle
349cc,** standard factory frame.
£12,800–13,500 *BKS*

r. **1961 AJS Model 31 CSR 646cc,**
two into one exhaust, alloy guards.
£2,750–3,000 *BLM*

1961 AJS DL31 De luxe 650cc, twin cylinder, excellent show order, totally restored.
£3,000–3,500 *SW*

1962 AJS Model 31, 646cc touring twin cylinder.
£2,250–2,650 *BLM*

1962 AJS Model 14 248cc, original unrestored condition.
£550–750 *PM*

1963 AJS Model 16 Short Stroke 348cc, good looking motor with enclosed push rods, a bit quicker than the long stroke motors.
£700–900 *BLM*

Revised 72 x 85.5mm bore and stroke dimensions compared to earlier engines which had 69 x 93mm.

1962 AJS Model 8 348cc, composite frame, steel stampings and tubular construction, largely complete, Swansea V5, requires full restoration.
£150–250 *S*

c1973 AJS Stormer Y4 Motocross 246cc, as found condition.
£240–280 *BKS*

The Stormer had explosive performance and was highly competitive in its day.

AMBASSADOR *(British 1947–64)*

1953 Ambassador 197cc, 2-stroke Villiers engine, original condition.
£500–750 *CRC*

ARIEL *(British 1902–70)*
The Leader 2-Stroke

By the mid-1950s Ariel had become part of the BSA group. Despite its earlier successes with the 4-strokes including the 198cc Colt 346 and 499cc Red Hunter singles, the 499cc Fieldmaster and 646cc Huntmaster twins and, last but not least, the 995cc Squariel Four, Ariel needed a new machine to progress into the future.

Fortunately the strong management team headed by Ken Whistance and Val Page was still in place at Ariel's Selly Oak, Birmingham, headquarters and after extensive market research they decided to design and build a 250cc twin cylinder, 2-stroke engine. It is worth noting that Ariel purchased a German-made Adler motorcycle of the same type for evaluation purposes. However, it was so well made, using many expensive components, that Ariel were unable to copy it exactly and still keep the price down to acceptable levels. Instead, they concentrated on the use of pressings, die-casting and plastic, the latter being truly innovative in

the motorcycle industry at this time.

Before going on sale on 17th July 1958, three black-painted prototypes of the Leader had been sent to mid-Wales for a series of gruelling test sessions. The Leader was in fact one of the best kept secrets of the British bike industry and created an instant sensation. Its 247cc twin engine offered smooth power, and other unique features made it outstanding. Subsequently the Arrow, Golden Arrow and 200 Arrow appeared – all without the rider protection of the Leader. Several of Ariel's 2-stroke twins were raced, one notably by Michael O'Rourke who finished 7th in the 1960 Lightweight TT on a bike tuned by Hermann Meier. One was even ridden to the summit of Ben Nevis – prepared and piloted by none other than trials star Sammy Miller.

Sadly, despite the gallant efforts of many to keep the marque alive it ceased to exist by the end of the 1960s.

1904 Ariel 334cc, belt-driven single speeder, professionally rebuilt in 1987 by Robin James of Leominster over a 5 year period, excellent condition throughout, modified back pedal brake, full history, restoration paperwork, old log books.
£7,800–8,200 *BKS*

1927 Ariel 350cc, hand change, 4-stroke.
£2,500–3,500 *CRC*

1929 Ariel Brooklands Sprint 499cc, small racing petrol tank, bronze dual chamber carburettor, Pilgrim oil pump, Albion gearbox, racing handlebars, fishtail exhaust, old and new style documents.
£4,750–5,250 *BKS*

r. **1930 Ariel Twin Port Sloper 498cc,** overhead valve, instrumentation in the tank panel includes speedometer and clock.
Est. £5,000–6,000 *BKS*

1931 Ariel 4F Square Four 498cc.
Est. £4,000–4,600 *S*

This 498cc 4F of 1931 is one of the first of Ariel's famous Square Four models.

1931 Ariel Model LB31 248cc, sloper engine of side valve configuration, 3 speed hand operated gearbox, requires restoration, remarkably sound order.
Est. £600–900 *S*

The price of this motorcycle when new in 1931 was £37.

1935 Ariel Square Four 601cc,
4 cylinder engine, overhead cam,
as found condition.
£3,500–4,000 *BKS*

1939 Ariel Red Hunter 346cc, used in recent years for VMCC
Hill Climb events.
£1,000–1,250 *BLM*

1938 Ariel Red Hunter 497cc,
overhead valve single, rigid frame,
girder forks.
£2,000–2,250 *BKS*

r. **1936 Ariel Square
Four 4F/600 601cc,**
original condition,
sound red and
black paintwork,
complete in all
respects, mechanical
condition unknown.
£3,000–3,500 *S*

> **Miller's is a price
> GUIDE not a price LIST**

1939 Ariel Twin Port 348cc, twin
high exhausts, paintwork in red and
chrome with black frame, carefully dry-
stored in ideal conditions for 20 years,
good and original condition throughout.
£2,400–2,600 *BKS*

r. **1949 Ariel Twin Cylinder 499cc,**
original specification in all major respects,
black paintwork, fair condition.
£600–850 *S*

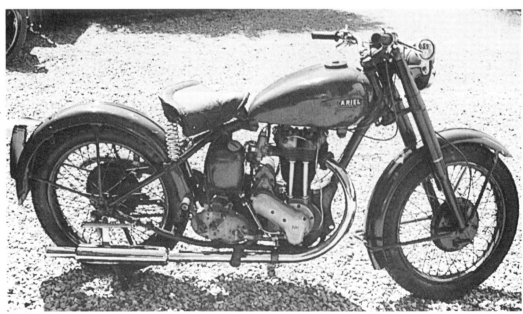

1945 Ariel NH Ex-War Department 350cc.
£1,000–1,200 *CStC*

1949 Ariel VG 499cc, 22bhp,
V5, original log book, original
and unspoilt example.
Est. £2,200–2,600 *BKS*

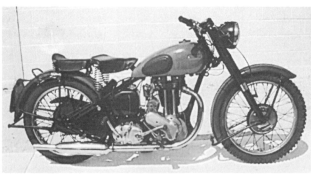

1951 Ariel VH Red Hunter 497cc,
overhead valve single, 4-speed, rigid frame.
£1,000–1,500 *BLM*

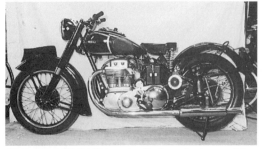

1949 Ariel MkI 1000cc, 4 cylinders, 2 pipe model,
all alloy engine.
£2,500–3,500 *CRC*

1951 Ariel NH Red Hunter 346cc.
£2,250–2,450 *BLM*

1954 Ariel Huntmaster 650cc, twin.
£2,000–3,000 *CRC*

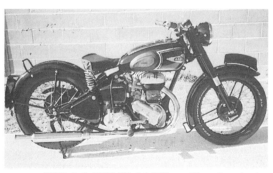

1951 Ariel VB Rigid 598cc, side valve single,
suitable for solo or sidecar use.
£2,250–2,650 *BLM*

Built from 1945 through to 1958.

l. **1955 Ariel Colt LH 198cc,** very original.
£325–475 *PM*

1955 Ariel Colt 198cc, four-stroke,
unrestored, in good condition overall.
£175–375 *BKS*

l. **1955 Ariel Colt 197cc,** engine
described as good, renewal of bottom
end bearings, wiring loom and rewound
alternator, hand-painted in green.
£300–500 *BKS*

*The Colt was built from 1954 through
to 1959.*

1955 Ariel Square Four 4G MkII 995cc, overhead valve engine, traditional Ariel Maroon with Burman gearbox, good condition throughout, no known modifications from original maker's specification.
£4,200–4,800 *BKS*

1957 Ariel NH Red Hunter 346cc, good steady singles.
£2,000–2,450 *BLM*

1957 Ariel KH Fieldmaster 499cc.
£1,500–2,000 *BLM*

This is the final model of 500 Ariel twins with full width hubs and headlamp cowl.

1958 Ariel Square Four 998cc, pivoted front fork frame and twin leading shoe front brakes, accurate in specification and finished to its original colours.
£3,000–3,400 *BKS*

The Square Four engine was exactly as the name suggests, four of everything up top.

1958 Ariel NH Red Hunter 346cc.
£2,000–2,350 *BLM*

The NH was built from 1945 to 1959.

1959 Ariel Leader 250cc, twin cylinder, two-stroke.
£750–1,250 *CRC*

1960 Ariel Leader 247cc.
£1,200–1,600 *BLM*

1959 Ariel Colt 198cc, concours condition.
£1,200–1,400 *PS*

1960 Ariel Leader 250cc, red and white livery, restored 10 years ago to concours order, features the bumper, indicators, side panels and luggage panniers characterised by this model.
£700–1,000 *BKS*

Designed by a team led by Ariel's Val Page, the Leader's 250cc 2-stroke twin engine was inspired by a German Adler twin and first appeared in 1958. It combined agile handling and a respectable speed with clean, quiet convenience, and its beam-type chassis carried panelling enveloping both the engine and much of the rear wheel.

1961 Ariel Arrow STD 247cc, 2-stroke twin.
£900–950 *BLM*

This sporting Arrow is fitted with Clubman handlebars and factory Avon full sports fairing.

l. **1961 Ariel Golden Arrow 247cc,** finished in cream and gold, good tidy order throughout, mechanical condition is unknown, no modifications, Swansea V5 and old log book.
£1,000–1,500 *BKS*

1963 Ariel Leader 250cc, all extras, including original tool kit and paint.
£2,500–2,700 *PC*

1960 Ariel Arrow 247cc, fully restored, very good condition throughout, V5, old style log book.
Est. £850–1,000 *BKS*

1965 Ariel Sports Arrow 247cc, 2-stroke twin.
£1,500–1,700 *BLM*

Often known as the Golden Arrow with its Clubman handlebars and sport's screen.

1962 Ariel Golden Arrow 247cc, 2-stroke, air-cooled, pressed steel frame and front fork attachment, good condition.
£500–600 *BKS*

AUTOMOTO
(French 1901–62)

1928 Automoto 249cc, powered by a Zurcher of Paris 248cc single cylinder, air-cooled, overhead valve engine, hand-change 2-speed gearbox, auxilliary oil hand pump, equipped with sports handlebars, original bike in original black livery, equipped tool box, luggage carrier and girder fork, coil spring front suspension, restoration project.
£1,000–1,200 *BKS*

BENELLI (Italian 1911–89)

Benelli was founded in 1911 by six brothers, who owned a small workshop in Pesaro on the Adriatic coast. Initially they confined their activities to repairing cars and motorcycles, but soon their engineering skills were extended to virtually anything mechanical – even guns – and they soon started to manufacture their own spare parts for cars and aircraft, a process accelerated by the outbreak of the Great War in 1914.

With the end of hostilities the company turned its focus on a new field — two wheels. They conceived a 98cc 2-stroke engine to power a very basic cycle. The engine out-performed the running gear, so the next logical step was to build a frame to withstand the engine's performance.

Thus came about the first complete Benelli motorcycle. Introduced in 1921, the newcomer featured a full loop frame, large wheels and girder front forks. The success of the first model soon resulted in the production of a more powerful 147cc version.

Over the next few years Benelli rose to become one of the largest bike builders in Italy, helped no doubt by track successes, including the Italian European championships. Irishman Ted Mellors also gained a prestigious TT victory in 1939.

This winning streak was carried over into the post-WWII period and Benelli rider Dario Ambrosini became the 1950 250cc world champion. A fatal accident whilst practising for the 1951 French Grand Prix saw the Italian marque withdraw from racing until 1959, when it returned with up-dated 250 singles ridden by Duke, Dale and Grassetti. Lack of success with these models led to the design and development of a 4 cylinder model, culminating in Benelli's second world title in 1969 (Carruthers).

After De Tomaso took over in the early 1970s, Benelli built and marketed a series of Japanese-inspired ohc roadster fours and sixes from 250 up to 900cc. There was also a wide range of lightweight motorcycles, scooters and mopeds, but all these smaller machines were powered by 2-stroke engines.

In 1989 De Tomaso sold Benelli to a local machine tool manufacturer, who subsequently produced a new range of 50cc models from a mini-bike to a sportster named the Devil.

1936 Benelli 250 Super Sport 247cc, overhead camshaft, twin port single, exposed hairpin valve springs, good condition.
£3,300–4,000 PC

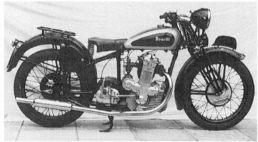

1937 Benelli 250 Sport 247cc, overhead camshaft, bore and stroke 67 x 70mm, finned sump, dynamo lighting.
£3,800–4,200 IVC

Cross Reference
Racing Bikes

1974 Benelli 250 2C 231.3cc, 2-stroke vertical twin cylinder, compression ratio of 10:1, 2/22mm Dell'Orto carburettors, 25bhp at 6850rpm, 5-speed gearbox with wet multi-plate clutch, 180mm twin front brakes, rear single 160mm, top speed of 145kmh, frame, forks, engine and gearbox in good working order, red paintwork, tank and mudguards in fair condition.
£100–200 BKS

1977 Benelli 750 SEI Racer 747.7cc, racerised version of standard roadster, special tank and seat, clip-ons, 6 pipes, uprated motor.
£2,500–3,000 PC

1978 Benelli 354 Sport 345cc, specially made café racer, with wire wheels, 2LS drum front brake, racing tank and seat.
Est. £2,500–2,800 *S*

In March 1996 the weekly paper Motor Cycle News *reported that the famous Benelli marque was to be given a new lease of life with an investment from Merloni.*

1981 Benelli 354 Sport 345cc, transverse overhead camshaft 4 cylinder, black livery, good condition throughout, modifications from factory specification.
£600–700 *BKS*

The Benelli factory at Pesaro was for many years controlled by the Benelli family who also owned Motobi, but more recently (and like Moto Guzzi) were headed in the 1970s by Alessandro de Tomaso.

1979 Benelli 500 Quattro 498cc, brand new, unregistered, essentially Italian copy of Honda CB500/4.
£2,000–2,500 *PC*

1981 Benelli Quattro 231cc, seized front brake caliper, otherwise good condition.
Est. £1,400–1,800 *BKS*

Revitalised after its takeover in 1971 by Argentine industrialist Alessandro de Tomaso, Benelli launched a range of new 6 and 4 cylinder sports bikes. Smallest of these Honda-inspired machines was the 254 (250 4 cylinder) Quattro which, when deliveries commenced in 1979, was the most expensive 250 on sale in Britain. The 231cc Quattro is the most collectable of Benelli's various models from the 1970–80 period.

BMW *(German 1920–)*

c1938 BMW R5 494cc, overhead valve.
£5,500–6,000 *AtMC*

1962 BMW R69S 594cc, engine valve guides and springs renewed and valves reground, cylinder rebored, condition good, 4 speed footchange gearbox, rear luggage carrier, crashbars and rear view mirror, frame, gearbox and electrics good, black BMW livery paintwork largely original, apart from stainless steel exhaust pipes and silencers, no known modifications.
£4,600–5,200 *BKS*

BIANCHI *(Italian 1897–1967)*

1956 Bianchi Tonale 174.73cc, bore and stroke 60 x 61.8mm, chain driven single overhead camshaft, original model, missing exhaust system.
£750–900 *IVC*

1973 BMW R50/5 498cc, crash bars fitted, reliable and regularly serviced, good condition, very good black BMW livery.
£1,500–1,800 *BKS*

BOWN *(British 1950–58)*

1952 Bown Lightweight 98cc, two-stroke air-cooled unit, 3 speed gearbox, electric lighting and drum brakes, fully restored. **Est. £900–1,200** *BKS*

Formerly under the Aberdale trademark, Bown made autocycles and lightweight motorcycles until about 1955.

BRIDGESTONE *(Japanese 1952–early '70s)*

1968 Bridgestone Dual Twin 175cc, disc valve induction twin cylinder two-stroke, 5 speed gearbox, chrome bore barrels and reported to be very smooth in running, completely restored to concours condition. **£2,500–2,750** *BKS*

This machine won the best two-stroke award at the 1995 Isle of Man TT week concours event.

BROUGH-SUPERIOR *(British 1921–40)*

1936 Brough-Superior SS80 998cc, large capacity, side valve, V-twin, thorough mechanical overhaul, new pistons, flywheels, transmission sound, mag-dyno overhauled and new saddle covers fitted, all-weather finish paintwork, modifications from the machine's original specification are the substitution of the Druid fork central spring for a telescopic unit, replacement of the front brake with an earlier and larger Brough item. **£10,000–12,000** *S*

1936 Brough-Superior SS80 998cc. **£11,000–14,000** *VER*

Although this machine is not as exclusive as the famed SS100, the SS80 is highly prized today. Brough-Superior was known for many years as the 'Rolls-Royce of Motorcycles'.

1968 Bridgestone Sport 90cc, 4 speed rotary gearbox, frame Italian-style 'hump back' pressed steel, restored to correct specification. **£1,200–1,400** *BKS*

This may be the only Bridgestone Sport 90cc in the UK.

BROWN *(British 1902–19)*

1907 Brown 3.5hp 500cc, engine restored and running, horn, lamp, cane pillion, stands, a spare engine and front suspension unit, imported from New Zealand, partially restored. **Est. £4,000–6,000** *BKS*

Brown Brothers, the motor factors of Great Eastern Street, London EC, who are still active in this field, albeit as part of the Dana Group today, built motorcycles of standard design and fitted engines of 350cc and 500cc up until around 1916.

BSA *(British 1906–7, late 1970s–)*
Gold Star Profile

Few motorcycles can be everything to everyone but the BSA Gold Star – the Goldie – come closer than most. A 100mph lap at Brooklands Clubman's racing, scrambling, trials, street bike the legendary Goldie could cope with almost anything. Its origin goes back to 1937 when, on the final day of June, the famous TT rider Wal Handley won a Brooklands Gold Star for lapping at over 100mph on a 500cc iron engined BSA Empire Star specially prepared by tuners Jack Arnott and Len Crisp to run on dope. In fact, Handley's race winning average speed was 102.27mph, with a best lap of 105.57mph on the Surrey banking. This outstanding performance resulted in the Empire Star title being dropped in favour of the Gold Star for the 1938 model year.

Three versions were offered, standard, competition and racing. Light alloy was used for the cylinder and head with screw-in valve seats and the pushrod tower was an integral part of the castings. An Amal TT carburettor was standardised and, most surprising of all, the gearbox shell was cast in magnesium alloy. For the following year the gearbox shell reverted to aluminium but there was the advantage of an optional close ratio cluster.

The 1939 Gold Star was the last for nine years. The war meant that the production requirement was for the side valve M20 military models rather than the expensive limited run sportster, however good. After the conflict the factory concentrated on the B31/33 tourers which were then fitted with telescopic forks. A competition model, the B32 fitted with an iron engine, was offered for trials.

The next development in the Gold Star story came in 1948 when high performance versions of the B31/33 range were offered rather than direct descendants of the pre-war M24. The 350 model had an alloy cylinder and head, known as the ZB32, these engines were long stroke with internal dimensions of 71 x 88mm. At this stage a 500 version was at least planned but it is doubtful if any were actually built until later. This was designated B34 and based on the 350 but with an 85mm bore.

The full 500 (499cc) was in production by 1950 with a power output of 33bhp, the smaller engine's power was up to 25bhp by this time. It should be remembered that this was in the days of 'pool' petrol which had a very low octane rating. The chassis had also received attention to keep it in line with the extra power and now featured plunger rear suspension and more stopping power thanks to a new 8in front brake.

In the Clubman's TT the 350 in particular was so dominant from 1949 to 1957 that the class became a Gold Star benefit and was axed. Meanwhile, the BSA work's scrambles and trials teams were also proving almost unbeatable.

The engines had detail changes for 1951 including die-cast head, cylinder and bolt on rocker boxes. The following year saw the BB32 with plunger suspension but most important were the mechanical changes. Valve angles were changed from 37 to 33 degrees with both inlet and exhaust valve diameters increased and their ports opened up to match. To take advantage of this, a larger Amal TT9 carburettor was fitted. A test of the new BB32 in *Motor Cycling* found maximum speed to be 98mph.

When the 1953 model was announced, BSA revealed that the GS models were to be considerably revised. Under the B prefix, the new Goldies featured duplex cradle frames and swing arm suspension. One year later the CB arrived, distinguishable by its massive engine finning. This motor had a shorter conrod and oval flywheel to clear the piston. Valve adjustment was carried out by an eccentric rocker spindle to cut down on reciprocating weight and an Amal GP was specified for the first time. Power was increased to 30bhp at 6800rpm on the 350 and the 500 kicked out 37bhp at 6600rpm. Other changes included a timed engine breather, EN36 crankpin and Nimonic 80 exhaust valve and finally the Clubman version of both the 350 and 500 had clip-ons as standard equipment.

Virtually the last stage of development came in 1956 with the introduction of a 190mm front brake and 1½in GP carburettor for the 500 which pumped out 42bhp at 7000rpm. There was also the 646cc twin cylinder Rocket Gold Star, but this was only built in 1962 and 1963. So came to an end perhaps the famous of all BSA's many models.

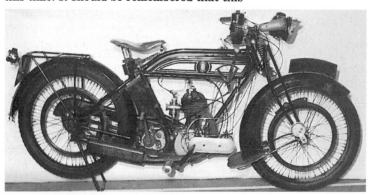

l. **1923 BSA 350cc.** **£3,400–3,800** *PS*

Founded in 1906, Birmingham Small Arms (BSA) soon established itself as Britain's premier motorcycle marque, a position it held until the late 1960s.

1915 BSA 557cc Model K, 4½hp engine, 3 speed gearbox, complete engine overhaul, parts generally sound, requiring restoration.
£2,500–3,000 *BKS*

1924 BSA 350cc, acetylene lighting set, finished in correct BSA livery, restored.
£2,200–2,600 *BKS*

1925 BSA Model B 250cc, 2-speed gearbox, dual rear brake, good condition.
£1,800–2,000 *BKS*

A top-selling model for BSA in the 1920s, the versatile Model B, or 'Round Tank' as it came to be known, was used by just about every tradesman whose job required cheap personal transport.

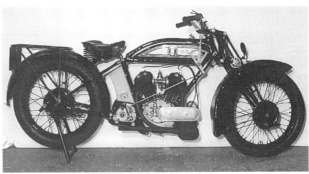

1927 BSA E27 Light Side Valve 770cc V-Twin, original engine, part restored.
£2,000–2,500 *PS*

It is alleged to be the only 770cc light model in Britain.

> A rebuilt motorcycle is not necessarily more valuable than a motorcycle in good original condition, even if the restoration has been costly.

1927 BSA 500cc, original condition, good running order.
£3,250–3,750 *CstC*

1929 BSA Sports Sloper 500cc, overhead valve, twin port, hand gear change, original condition, restored tank.
£2,500–3,500 *CRC*

1932 BSA Blue Star, overhead valve, twin port.
£2,000–3,000 *CRC*

1934 BSA B12 250cc, overhead valve engine, hand gear change.
£1,000–2,000 *CRC*

1935 BSA B35-3 De Luxe 249cc, bore and stroke 63 x 80mm, restored.
£1,200–1,400 *BKS*

It is believed BSA produced only 256 of this model.

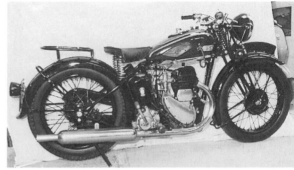

1935 BSA M20 500cc, single cylinder, side valve, hand gearchange.
£1,750–2,750 *CRC*

1936 BSA Solo B20 249cc, mechanically sound, good original condition.
Est. £2,200–2,600 *S*

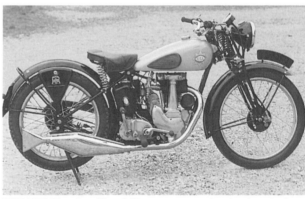

1938 BSA B22 Empire Star 249cc, sports overhead valve single cylinder engine.
£2,800–3,000 *BLM*

Superbly restored example of BSA pre-war 250 overhead valve single.

Don't Forget!

If in doubt please refer to the 'How to Use' section at the beginning of this book.

1927 BSA 350cc, single cylinder.
£2,000–2,350 *AT*

For many years this motorcycle was used for display at a London cycle shop.

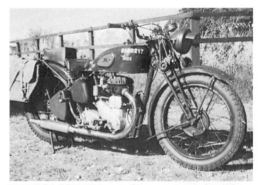

1942 BSA M20 500cc, military motorcycle with side valve single cylinder engine, fitted field stand, headlamp shield and pannier bags.
£1,800–2,000 *BLM*

1946 BSA C11G 249cc, overhead valve engine, complete, needing restoration.
£300–400 *MAY*

1947 BSA A7 500cc, twin cylinder, rigid back end.
£2,000–3,000 *CRC*

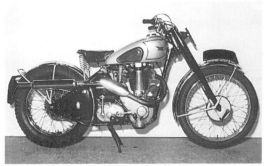

1947 BSA B32 Trials 348cc, overhead valve
cylinder engine, original condition.
£1,700–2,000 *PS*

*Alleged to be the second oldest of these much
sought-after models and originally sold by Yeovil
Motor Mart in January 1947, this machine is
standard except for the 18in rear wheel.*

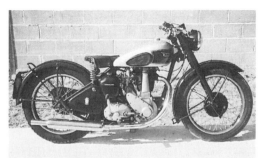

1948 BSA B31 Rigid 348cc.
£1,650–1,850 *BLM*

*The first B31 appeared in 1945. For 1948,
a number of changes appeared including
transferring the speedo from its tank
mounting to the handlebars.*

1948 BSA ZB32 GS Trials 348cc, rigid framed
competition model.
£2,650–2,850 *BLM*

1950 BSA B31 348cc, original machine, finished
in green and chrome, telescopic forks, rigid back
end, Swansea V5 document.
£1,400–1,600 *BKS*

1950 BSA ZB32 Gold Star Trials 348cc,
comprehensive overhaul, original green and chrome
petrol tank, black frame, A1 in all respects.
£2,200–2,400 *S*

*The Gold Star was one of the most versatile
machines ever produced, being built in roadster,
clubman's racer, scrambler and trials form.*

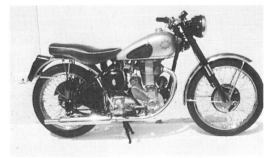

1951 BSA B32 Gold Star 348cc, smart
plunger Goldie.
£3,500–4,000 *BLM*

1951 BSA ZB31 348cc, rigid rear end, telescopic front forks, later period carburettor, extensively restored.
£1,800–2,000 *BKS*

Miller's is a price GUIDE
not a price LIST

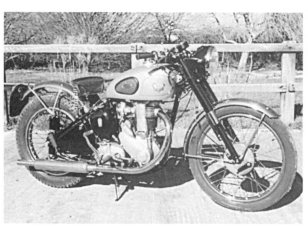

1951 BSA B34 Gold Star 499cc, early roadster, with plunger frame.
£4,300–4,500 *BLM*

1952 BSA D1 Bantam 123cc,
single cylinder, 2-stroke.
£500–550 *BKS*

1952 BSA A7 497cc, twin cylinder, overhead valve engine, red livery, good original condition.
£1,200–1,400 *BKS*

1952 BSA Gold Flash 650cc, twin cylinder, plunger rear suspension.
£2,000–3,000 *CRC*

1952 BSA A10 Golden Flash 646cc, plunger frame, twin exhausts, chrome-plated tank panels.
£2,000–3,000 *BLM*

This A10 is largely the same as when it left the Birmingham factory.

c1953 D1 BSA Bantam 123cc, plunger type rear suspension, restored to high standard throughout, painted green with cream tank panels.
Est. £500–800 *S*

BSA offered the D1 Bantam with the option of either a rigid or plunger rear end to the frame.

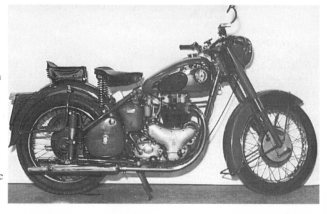

r. **1953 BSA A7 497cc,** authentic and unrestored.
£2,000–2,500 *PS*

1953 BSA M21 596cc, big side valve workhorse.
£1,250–1,550 *BLM*

1953 BSA D1 Bantam 123cc, fully sprung,
finished in traditional green and cream livery,
excellent condition.
£750–800 *S*

1953 BSA D1 Bantam 123cc,
no known modifications, original
specification, green and cream,
good condition.
£700–850 *BKS*

*The D1 was the first in a long line
of Bantam models built by BSA.
It first appeared in 1948.*

1954 BSA B31 348cc, swinging fork frame,
burgundy and chrome, concours condition.
£2,000–2,500 *BLM*

1954 BSA B31 348cc.
£1,400–1,700 *BLM*

*The change to swinging fork frame was
introduced in 1954.*

1954 BSA B33 499cc, pushrod, 23bhp at
5500rpm, 4 speed gearbox, all chain transmission,
extensive restoration, excellent condition.
Est. £2,200–2,600 *S*

> **Did you know?**
>
> *MILLER'S Classic Motorcycles Price
> Guide builds up year-by-year to form
> the most comprehensive photo-reference
> library system available.*

1954 BSA B31 348cc, single cylinder, overhead valve,
original specification, rebuilt 1983, running well.
£1,000–1,400 *PS*

Now converted to 499cc capacity.

1954 BSA B33 499cc, swinging
arm, headlamp cowl, Gold Star
type front brake.
£2,000–2,300 *BLM*

1954 BSA B31 348cc.
£2,300–2,500 *BLM*

The last of plunger framed B31/33 series.

1954 BSA B31 Trials Trim 348cc, iron head
and barrel engine, plunger frame B31 converted
to Gold Star Trials specification.
£1,800–2,300 *BLM*

1954 BSA B33 499cc, single cylinder,
overhead valve engine, standard trim
touring model, finished in maroon,
correct specification.
£1,800–2,000 *BKS*

*BSA made a succession of singles from
the sporty Goldie to the lightweight.
Amongst the mid-range was the famous
B31 and the lesser known B33 overhead
valve 500cc single, which is possibly
the most useful of all the singles BSA
ever made.*

1955 BSA M21 596cc, plunger frame and pillion pad.
£1,000–1,250 *PM*

*The M21 was manufactured from 1937 until 1963.
Suitable for solo or sidecar use.*

1955 BSA BB34 Gold Star 500cc, scrambler
gearbox, mechanically overhauled, super condition.
Est. £2,500–3,000 *S*

1955 BSA C10L 249cc, side
valve engine.
Est. £750–850 *BKS*

*The C10L was the cheapest of
the BSAs 250cc range. In
1957 the C10 was dropped
from their production.*

> **Miller's is a price GUIDE
> not a price LIST**

r. **1956 BSA C10 249cc,** side
valve, single cylinder, plunger
rear suspension, rewired, new
piston, lighting switch, rear
wheel sprocket, new tyres, fair
condition, excellent order.
£750–800 *PS*

*Non-standard due to the
Bantam front end, this C10
side valver is none the less in
excellent condition.*

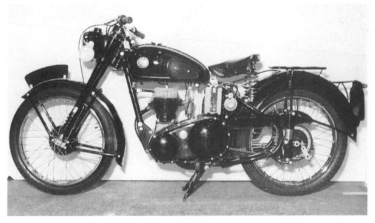

1956 BSA DB34 Clubman's Gold Star 499cc,
Amal concentric MkI carburettor.
£6,500–6,800 *BLM*

1956 BSA B31 348cc.
£1,300–1,700 *BLM*

*The B31 of 1956 and 1957 featured full
width alloy hubs and cowled headlamp.
Mag-dyno looked after the electrics.*

1956 BSA B31 348cc, Ariel-type brakes,
alloy brake hubs, headlamp nacelle,
mudguards, all original.
£1,650–1,850 *BLM*

1956 BSA Gold Star 499cc, CB350
frame of 1956 vintage fitted with
later 499cc DBD500 engine, RRT2
gearbox, 190mm front brake, good
order throughout.
£5,800–6,000 *BKS*

*BSA found fame with Gold Star. The
machines come from the era of the
coffee bar rider and the time when the
enthusiast was free to enjoy the roads
and the freedom of motorcycling was
probably at its best. The 'Goldie' is,
and always will be, a true classic.*

1956 BSA B31 348cc, totally original except Amal
concentric carburettor.
£2,000–2,500 *BLM*

1956 BSA B33 499cc, overhead valve single,
original condition.
£900–1,200 *BKS*

*It can be said that the B series of single BSAs were
the workhorses of the range, solid dependable and
economic they served the population in many roles.
'Swinging arm' became standard in 1956, with Ariel-
type full width hubs also introduced and the gear
ratios were made closer, thus livening performance.*

1956 BSA A10 Golden Flash 646cc, this machine
has been the subject of a full restoration and has
seen very little use since, included in rebuild was
engine, front forks and black paintwork.
£3,500–3,800 *BKS*

r. **1957 BSA Gold Star 350cc,** single cylinder,
Clubman trim, restored.
£5,000–7,500 *CRC*

1957 BSA Road Rocket 650cc, sports version of
A10, parallel twin, TT carburettor, Ariel-type
front hubs.
£3,000–4,000 *CRC*

1957 BSA A7 497cc, non-standard
mudguards, headlamp, sweptback
Gold Star pattern exhaust pipes and
silencers, good mechanical condition,
runs well.
£1,500–1,800 *BKS*

1958 BSA D5 Bantam 172cc, 1966
engine fitted, maroon with cream tank
panels, restored.
Est. £600–650 *BKS*

*In 1958 BSA upgraded to the D5 which
meant an increase in engine size to 172cc
and a general 'beefing' up all round*

1958 BSA A7SS Shooting Star 500cc,
twin cylinder.
£2,500–3,500 *CRC*

1958 BSA Super Rocket 650cc, correct to
standard specification, good order,
mechanically sound.
Est. £2,500–2,800 *BKS*

1958 BSA C12 249cc.
£750–850 *MR*

*The last of BSA's pre-unit singles. Built
from 1956 to 1958 before being replaced
by C15.*

1958 BSA A7SS Shooting Star 497cc, sports
version of A7.
£3,000–4,000 *BLM*

c1959 BSA C15 247cc, green with
black frame, restored to very good
mechanical and cosmetic condition.
£1,200–1,400 *S*

*Originally conceived as a ride-to-
work commuter, the C15 was later
used for a wide variety of tasks
including road racing, scrambling,
trials, grass track racing, even
sprinting and record breaking.*

1959 D7 BSA Bantam 172cc,
in good order.
Est. £600–700 *BKS*

*Part of the famous Bantam range
produced by BSA between 1948
and 1972, it is said that nearly one
million of the model were made in
various guises.*

1959 BSA B31 348cc, alternator model.
£1,500–2,000 *CStC*

1959 BSA DB32 Clubman's Gold Star 348cc.
£6,250–6,850 *BLM*

*A smaller engined version of the Gold Star
Clubman's is much rarer than the 500 model.*

1959 BSA 250 C15 247cc.
£500–600 *PM*

*The humble pushrod C15 was Britain's
best selling 250 during the late 1950s and
early 1960s.*

1959 BSA A10 Super Rocket 650cc,
tank recently restored, modified with
sweptback exhaust pipes, Gold Star
silencers, clip-on handlebars, alloy
mudguards, fork gaiters, Gold Star
clocks, headlamp, good order.
£2,400–2,600 *BKS*

1959 BSA C15 250cc.
£400–450 *AT*

c1960 BSA A10 Super Road Rocket 646cc,
A10 Super Rocket engine, 350 Gold Star frame,
finished in café racer style, dropped handlebars,
humped seat, twin leading-shoe BSA brakes,
speedo and tachometer, Goldie silencers,
chromed petrol tank, good unrestored condition.
£2,000–2,400 *S*

l. **1960 BSA C15 247cc,** overhead valve, ex-police,
black and chrome finish, good mechanical order.
£850–950 *MAY*

1960 BSA C15 247cc, overhead valve, unit construction, 4 speed gearbox.
£480–520 *BKS*

1960 BSA D7 Bantam 172cc.
£500–600 *BLM*
The Bantam D7 was introduced in 1959.

1960 BSA Super Rocket 646cc, sports version of A10, overhead valve twin, engine overhaul, new camshaft, valves fitted, non-original front mudguard.
£2,200–2,400 *BKS*

1960 BSA A7SS Shooting Star 497cc.
£2,000–2,200 *BLM*
The A7SS (Shooting Star) is basically the same as larger A10 except for a smaller engine capacity.

1960 BSA A7 Shooting Star 497cc, original specification except for later twin leading shoe front brake, totally restored to concours condition.
£3,000–3,500 *PC*

1960 BSA A7 497cc, good chrome with red and black paintwork, very good overall condition.
£1,800–2,000 *S*
BSA's A7 parallel twin earned an enviable reputation for reliability, performance and handling.

1960 BSA Super Rocket 646cc, modified for touring, raised handlebars, screen, crash bars, rear carrier, top box, pannier mounts, updated with halogen headlight, twin leading shoe front brake, controls/switchgear and seat of later models.
£2,200–2,400 *BKS*

BSA's top 650 sportster until the advent of the Rocket Gold Star. The Super Rocket was built from 1958 to 1963.

1960 BSA A10 Spitfire Scrambler 650cc.
£7,500–8,000 *CStC*
Very rare in England being one of 1200 built for export only.

1960 BSA Gold Flash 650cc, not original but good useable bike.
£1,200–1,800 *CStC*

1960 BSA DBD34 Gold Star 500cc, single cylinder Clubman's trim.
£700–800 *CRC*

1960 BSA A7SS 500cc.
£2,000–2,500 *CStC*

c1960 BSA DBD34 Gold Star 499cc, full race specification includes race tuned engine, 1⅛in Amal GP carburettor, 5 gallon Lyta alloy tank, 190mm front brake and alloy rims.
Est. £5,500–6,000 *BKS*

1961 BSA A7SS Shooting Star 497cc, fully restored to original specification.
£3,000–3,200 *BLM*

1961 BSA D7 Bantam 175cc, sound original condition.
£200–400 *S*

The D7 model was manufactured between 1959–66. It featured a new pivoted fork frame, Tiger Cub-type forks and revised styling.

1961 BSA A10 Golden Flash 647cc, good touring machine.
£3,250–3,450 *BLM*

> **A rebuilt motorcycle is not necessarily more valuable than a motorcycle in good original condition, even if the restoration has been costly.**

l. **1961 BSA A10 Golden Flash 650cc,** 2 cylinder.
£2,000–3,000 *CRC*

1961 BSA C15 Trials 247cc.
£1,500–1,800 *BKS*

These machines were ridden to many victories by BSA factory riders, including the Lampkin brothers and Jeff Smith.

1961 BSA C15 247cc.
£400–450 *CStC*

1961 BSA B40 343cc, single cylinder, telescopic forks, sprung frame, 4 speed manual posi-stop gearbox, painted in royal red, mechanically very good condition, Swansea V5.
Est. £1,100–1,300 *BKS*

Larger version of the popular C15 model.

1962 BSA Bantam D1 125cc, 2-stroke.
£500–1,000 *CRC*

1962 BSA A10 Golden Flash 646cc, overhead twin.
Est. £1,350–1,450 *BKS*

1962 BSA A50 499cc.
£1,600–1,800 *PS*

The new unit construction A50 (and larger A65) twins were introduced in January 1962. This early example has a later model seat and lacks the original side panel badges, otherwise is largely ex-works.

1962 BSA Super Rocket 650cc, overhead valve pre-unit twin, optional rev counter, non-standard front mudguard and headlamp.
£3,800–4,200 *IVC*

1963 BSA A10 Rocket Gold Star 650cc, last pre-unit twin, RRT2 gearbox.
£6,000–7,500 *CRC*

r. **1963 BSA Rocket Gold Star 646cc,** Siamese pipes, 190mm front brake.
£4,000–6,000 *BLM*

Twin engine version of Gold Star. Only made in 1962/63.

1963 BSA C15 247cc, original and complete, finished in red, Swansea V5 and MOT.
Est. £500–800 *S*

Introduced in 1958 as a replacement for the C12, BSA's new unit single proved to have considerable development potential, spawning a whole series of machines that would ultimately result in the B50 models of the 1970s.

1963 BSA Rocket Gold Star 646cc, overhead valve Clubman's specification including clip-ons, 190mm front brake and alloy rims.
£6,500–7,500 *IVC*

1964 BSA B40 343cc.
£900–950 *PM*

A larger engined version of C15, it offers more torque and superior power to weight ratio.

1963 BSA Rocket Gold Star 646cc, overhead valve twin, 190mm front brake, touring rim, good original specification.
£6,000–7,500 *IVC*

1965 BSA B40 Star 343cc, overhead unit construction single, 4 speed gearbox.
£1,200–1,300 *BLM*

The B40 production ceased in 1965.

1964 BSA Beagle 75cc, substantially original and complete.
Est. £800–1,000 *BKS*

Powered by a single cylinder four-stroke engine the Beagle could cruise at 40mph and achieve 150mpg.

1965 BSA D7 Bantam De Luxe 175cc, restored D7, original condition.
£650–750 *BLM*

1965 BSA D7 172cc, this hybrid machine has a 1965 D7 chassis with later D10 4-speed engine fitted.
£350–450 *MR*

1965 BSA A65 Rocket 654cc, Siamesed exhaust, single carburettor, with matching instruments.
£2,000–2,200 *BLM*

1965 BSA D7 Bantam 172cc, finished in black, Swansea V5.
£480–520 *BKS*

1965 was the final year of the D7 model.

1965 BSA B44 GP Motocross 440cc, catalogue restoration.
£3,500–4,000 *PC*

Production replica of factory rider Jeff Smith's world championship winning machine.

1966 BSA Bantam D7 173cc, modified for trials use.
£540–620 *PS*

1967 BSA Barracuda 247cc, overhead valve.
£850–950 *MAY*

1965 BSA Cyclone A50 497cc.
£2,000–2,300 *BLM*

This is a rare twin carburettor version of the A50 unit construction model.

1966 A65 Spitfire MKII 654cc.
£2,500–3,500 *CRC*

1967 BSA A65T Thunderbolt 654cc, twin cylinder.
£1,500–2,500 *CRC*

1968 BSA Shooting Star 441cc, single cylinder.
£1,000–1,500 *CRC*

1968 BSA B40 343cc, ex-army machine, similar to civilian version, changes include front brake and oil tank, both from competition models.
£500–600 *PM*

1968 BSA B25 247cc, very good condition.
£1,000–1,500 *CStC*

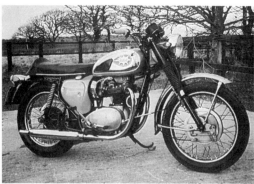

1968 BSA A65 Lightning 654cc, sports
version of A65 with twin carburettors and
twin leading shoe front brake.
£2,000–2,300 *BLM*

1969 BSA D14/4Bantam 175cc, two-stroke.
£500–1,000 *CRC*

1969 BSA B25 Starfire 247cc,
paintwork and chrome fair condition.
£850–950 *S*

1969 BSA A65 Spitfire MkIV 654cc, export model.
£3,500–4,000 *BLM*

*Previously owned by Robert Plant, of the group Led
Zeppelin, which he donated as a raffle prize for the benefit
of the Nordoff-Robbin's Music Therapy Centre.*

1969 BSA B25 Starfire 247cc.
£1,250–1,450 *BLM*

*The B25 Starfire was the American
name for the C25 Barracuda.*

1969 BSA A75R Rocket 740cc, 3 cylinder.
£3,000–4,000 *CRC*

1970 BSA Cheney Victor APP 500cc,
excellent original condition.
£2,500–3,000 *SW*

l. **1971 BSA A65T Thunderbolt 654cc.**
£1,500–2,500 *CRC*

BULTACO
(Spanish 1958–mid 1980s)

1972 Bultaco Matador 250 Enduro 244cc,
2-stroke single cylinder.
£700–900 *IVC*

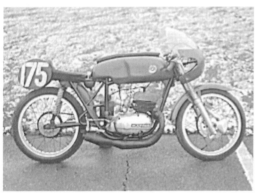

c1965 Bultaco TSS Solo 124cc.
Est. £2,200–2,800 *S*

Bultaco's 124cc TSS racing motorcycle met with considerable success during the 1960s both in the hands of the factory riders, notably Ramon Torras, and at club level to whom the machine's comparative simplicity, being a piston-ported single, was an advantage.

CONNAUGHT
(British 1910–27)

1923 Connaught 3½hp De Luxe, 3 speed
gearbox, all chain drive, unrestored.
£1,500–2,000 *BKS*

1923 Connaught 348cc, Burman 3-speed gearbox, chain drive,
fitted with running boards.
Est. £1,500–1,800 *BKS*

The Connaught motorcycle was made at Aston, Birmingham, by the Bordesley Engineering Company, who made various machines with maximum engine sizes of 350cc down to lightweight 2-stroke models.

CALTHORPE
(British 1911–39)

1929 Calthorpe Ivory Series I 348cc,
overhead valve.
£3,500–4,500 *VER*

This marque first appeared before WWI, its best known post-war bike being the Ivory seen here, which first appeared in 1929.

c1914 Calthorpe 249cc, JAP engine.
£4,500–5,000 *AtMC*

CECCATO *(Italy 1950–63)*

1952 Ceccato 125 Sport, overhead valve.
£750–950 *IVC*

The company was founded in 1950 and produced a wide range of models, with both 2- and 4-stroke engines.

COTTON (British 1919–80)

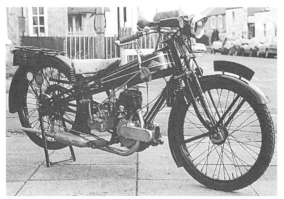

c1967 Cotton Telstar Racing 247cc,
7in twin leading shoe brake, introduced in
1964, 18in wheels fitted from 1967 onwards.
£1,400–1,800 *BKS*

*The Gloucester firm of Cotton became
famous in pre-war days for fine handling
sports bikes powered by JAP and
Blackburne engines.*

c1925 Cotton Blackburne 348cc.
£4,500–5,000 *AtMC*

COVENTRY-EAGLE
(British 1901–39)

1929 Coventry-Eagle Flying 8 996cc,
original condition.
£28,750–30,250 *BKS*

1933 Coventry-Eagle 249cc, 2-stroke Villiers
engine, twin port.
£1,500–2,500 *CRC*

CZ (Czechoslovakian 1932–)

1976 CZ Model 988 Enduro 246cc.
£450–500 *JCZ*

DKW (German 1919–81)

1938 DKW Solo 349cc, ex-German army, single
cylinder, used in north Africa, original condition.
£1,800–2,000 *C*

*This famous German manufacturer was founded in
1919 by Danish-born Joerge Skafte Rasmussen at
Zschopau, Chemnitz. This model is thought to be
extremely rare as most were built as twin cylinders.*

DERBI (Spain 1950–)

1980 DKW W2000 Rotary 294cc.
£2,000–2,250 *BLM*

*Sold in some markets as Hercules and
some as DKW.*

1975 Derbi Angel Nieto Replica Racing 49cc,
air-cooled, 6-speed, disc valve, 2-stroke.
£4,000–4,500 *PC*

DMW *(British 1945–71)*

1965 DMW Hornet Racing 247cc.
Est. £2,500–2,600 *BKS*

DOT *(British 1903–74)*

1946 DOT Tradesman's Tricycle 123cc, single cylinder, Villiers engine, chain final drive, front load platform supported by the 2 front wheels, running order.
£300–350 *S*

1946 DOT Tradesman's Tricycle 123cc, two-stroke Villiers engine, twin port.
£650–1,250 *CRC*

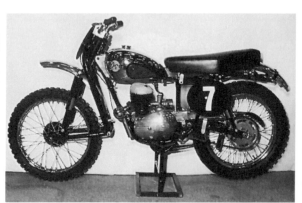

1954 DOT SCH Scrambler 197cc.
£1,000–1,500 *DOT*

l. **c1955 DOT Scrambler 197cc,** sound engine and transmission, fitted with lights, requires restoration.
Est. £600–900 *S*

Did you know?
MILLER'S Classic Motorcycles Price Guide *builds up year-by-year to form the most comprehensive photo-reference library system available.*

r. **1973 DOT Minarelli 170cc.**
£1,500–2,000 *DOT*
Eric Adcock ex-works bike.

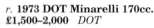

DOUGLAS
(British 1906–57)

The history of this marque began in 1906, when 27 year old William Douglas purchased the design of a flat twin cylinder engine from the Fairey company. While Fairey stopped motorcycle production for the next two years, Douglas was elevated to become one of the top British manufacturers.

Horizontal opposed engines were employed by over fifty motocycle companies, including ABC, BMW, Puch and Zündapp. Douglas chose a longitudinal arrangement for his twin. The advantages of Douglas's design were displayed at the 1912 TT, when riders Bashall and Kickham came first and second in the Junior (350cc) event.

The 2¾hp model was equipped with a flat 348cc twin cylinder engine. Power was transmitted by chain to a 2- or 3-speed gearbox of Douglas's own design, and by belt to the rear wheel. The characteristic feature of all Douglas machines at that time – a thin, large diameter 'bacon slicer' flywheel – was located on the nearside of the engine.

After WWI the Bristol-based company was successful in the 1923 TT, when Tom Sheard and Freddie Dixon won the first race for sidecar machines. Dixon was also responsible for a number of new roadsters in that decade, and also some very successful dirt-track machines.

By 1930 all models were flat twins, in three capacities and OHV and SV. The Endeavour arrived in 1935. This was their first real transverse twin and used a new 500cc engine which was also fitted to a more conventional model with fore and aft cylinders. A 2-stroke with a 148cc Villiers engine had been introduced at the end of 1932 and lasted most of the 1930s.

In 1935/36 the firm hit financial trouble and were rescued by the British Aircraft Company. Also Pride and Clark in London became sole agents for the marque. For a period they were sold under the Aero tag.

Only the 600 (596cc) twin was built in 1939 and then only in small numbers until the war broke out and the works turned to defence contracts. This enabled the company to build up its resources once again so that post-war they were able to return to the motorcycle field and the flat-twin engine, but from then on transversely mounted. This led to the T35, T350 (MkIII), Plus 80/90 and ultimately the Dragonfly. All was to no avail, and in March 1957 production of the flat-twins had ceased. The Vespa (which Douglas had begun importing in the late 1940s) continued to be sold, but to devotees of the marque it was the end.

c1912 Douglas 2¾hp 350cc.
£4,500–5,000 *AtMC*

1913 Douglas 2¾hp 350cc, complete, running order.
Est. £4,000–5,000 *BKS*

This machine took part in the 1987 Pioneer Run.

Cross Reference
Racing Bikes

1914 Douglas Veteran 2¾hp 350cc.
£5,500–6,000 *BLM*

Popular London to Brighton machine.

1922 Douglas Twin 2¾hp 350cc.
£4,000–4,500 *BLM*

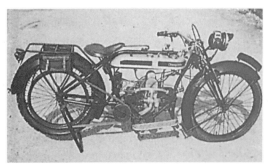

1924 Douglas 2¾hp 350cc, full lighting set and rear carrier fitted, finished in traditional Douglas livery of silver and blue for tank, other cycle parts black, sound mechanical condition.
£2,400–2,800 *S*

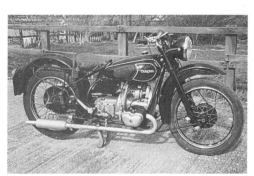

1948 Douglas T35 348cc.
£2,000–2,200 *BLM*

1951 Douglas MkV 348cc, flat twin, torsion bar rear suspension and different front forks.
£1,200–1,400 *BLM*

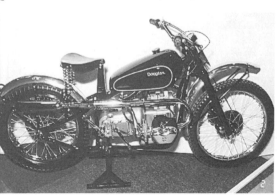

1951 Douglas Competition 348cc.
£3,000–4,000 *LDM*

1955 Douglas Dragonfly 348cc, overhead valve, flat twin, restored, mechanically sound.
Est. £2,500–2,750 *BKS*

1956 Douglas Dragonfly 348cc, Earles pivoted front forks, Girling convential rear damper units, alternator, headlamp nacelle extended from front of fuel tank, finished in black with red and gold lining, overhauled mechanically.
£2,000–2,200 *BKS*

1956 Douglas Dragonfly 348cc, good running order.
Est. £1,800–2,000 *BKS*

The Dragonfly model was introduced in 1954 and was a new approach by the factory who dispensed with their radiadraulic forks in favour of new Earles-type forks for this model.

1957 Douglas Dragonfly 348cc, flat-twin shaft drive to rear wheel, Earles-type forks, restored.
£1,600–1,800 *BKS*

In 1958 the factory was taken over by Westinghouse and the remaining stocks in the factory were sold in bulk.

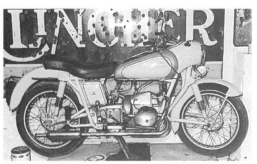

l. **1957 Douglas Dragonfly 348cc,** horizontal opposed overhead valve, twin cylinder, Earles-type front forks.
£1,500–2,500 *CRC*

1925 AJS Big Port 350cc, overhead valve.
£5,000–5,500 *VER*

1947 AJS Model 16M 348cc, telescopic forks
and rigid frame, popular reliable single.
£2,000–2,400 *BLM*

1938 AJS 350cc, 4-speed foot change gearbox,
to original specification, unrestored, good condition,
in black livery.
£1,500–2,000 *BKS*

c1928 AJS 1000cc, V-twin, side valve engine,
3-speed gearbox, sound condition, imported
from Eastern Europe.
£2,500–3,000 *BKS*

1953 AJS Model 18 497cc, overhead valve, single
cylinder, 4-speed gearbox, to original specification,
very good condition throughout.
£2,500–3,000 *BKS*

1957 AJS Model 30 593cc, overhead valve
twin engine, very good original condition.
£1,300–1,500 *PS*

1961 AJS Model 14 248cc, basically original but
non-standard headlamp and paintwork, in black
livery, requires restoration.
£700–800 *MWM*

1967 AJS Model 14 250cc,
non-standard alloy mudguards.
£1,000–1,200 *BLM*

1908 Ariel 2¾hp, with headlamp, painted black and white, owned by AOMCC.
£7,500–9,000 *AOC*

1930 Ariel Sloper 498cc, good overall condition, Swansea V5.
£3,500–4,500 *S*

A rare and fast motorcycle.

1930–40s Ariel W/NG 348cc, military model, single overhead valve.
£2,000–2,250 *BLM*

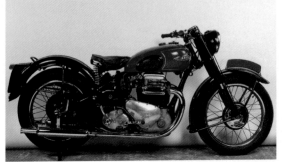

1953 Ariel Square Four 4G Mk1 995cc, smooth running condition.
£3,000–3,750 *BLM*

Although this is a 1953 model it has the iron top end from the earlier 1947/48 4G model.

1955 Ariel Square Four Model 4G Mk2 995cc, overhead camshaft and valves, Burman gearbox, to original maker's specification, good condition.
£3,400–3,700 *BKS*

1937 Ariel Red Hunter 346cc, restored 5 years ago, only 10,000 miles recorded since restoration, sprung saddle, headlamp, finished in black and red livery.
£2,750–3,250 *AOC*

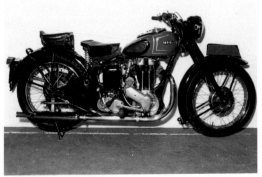

1947 Ariel NH 346cc, single cylinder, overhead valve, original and unrestored machine, good condition, only 4 registered owners from new, V5 log.
£1,800–2,200 *PS*

1962 Ariel Sports Arrow 247cc, with visor and headlamp, twin saddle, luggage carrier, finished in grey and gold livery.
£1,250–1,500 *AOC*

1971 Benelli 650 Tornado 642.8cc, overhead valve twin engine, drum brakes, 5-speed gearbox.
£1,800–2,100 *PC*

1976 Benelli 750 Sei 747.7cc, original, 6 exhaust pipes, concours condition.
£2,800–3,100 *PC*

1980 Benelli 254 Quattro 231cc, finished in red and yellow with dual seat and fairing.
£1,200–1,500 *PC*

The Mark 2 version of Benelli's famous 250, 4 cylinder street bike.

1952 BMW R25/2 247cc, plunger frame shaft drive, 4-speed gearbox, generator lighting, single sprung Denfeld saddle, finished in black and white livery.
£1,500–1,750 *PM*

1955 BMW 250 R25/3 247cc, air inlet under tank, no handshift lever, 18in (46cm) wheels.
£1,500–1,800 *PM*

This model was introduced in 1954 and discontinued at the end of 1955.

1962 Bianchi Tonale 174cc, overhead camshaft driven by a chain.
£1,500–2,000 *IMO*

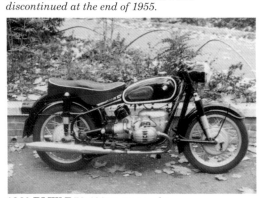

1960 BMW R50 490cc, restored to concours condition, finished in black livery.
£3,500–4,000 *BKS*

1980 BMW R80/7S 797.5cc, with spoke wheels.
£1,000–1,500 *PM*

Early R80/7 coded 'N' were built with wire wheels.

1926 Brough SS100 Pendine 998cc, V-twin, overhead valve, 4-stroke JAP engine, bore and stroke 80 x 99mm.
£25,000–30,000 *PM*

The SS100 was available to various specifications but only 20 racing Pendine models were built.

1936 Brough Superior SS80 1000cc, with model X Matchless V-twin engine, pillion seat, finished in black livery.
£14,000–15,000 *BLM*

1939 Brough Superior 1150cc, sprung frame model, with JAP engine, finished in black livery.
£12,000–13,000 *BLM*

1924 BSA Roundtank Model B 249cc, totally restored. **£2,000–2,500** *PVE*

Many of these BSA Roundtanks were manufactured, for GPO telegraph boys, and still in use post-WWII.

1936 BSA G14 1000cc, V-twin, hand gear change, panel tank and footboards.
£5,500–6,000 *BLM*

A good machine to use with a sidecar.

1925 BSA 3.49hp SV, single, side valve, restored, solid and reliable, luggage carrier.
£3,000–3,200 *BKS*

1939 BSA B21 249cc, girder forks, rigid frame, black paintwork.
£1,800–2,000 *PM*

1942 BSA WM20 496cc, side valve engine, foot change gearbox, a popular military machine.
£1,500–1,850 *BLM*

1953 BSA A7 Star Twin 497cc, with pillion seat, finished in maroon.
£2,500–3,000 *BLM*
This was the last of the plunger frame A7 models.

1954 BSA Gold Flash A10 647cc, with plunger frame.
£2,500–3,000 *BLM*
A well-loved solo or sidecar machine.

1958 BSA DB34 Gold Star 499cc, RRT2 close ratio gearbox, 190mm front brake, alloy wheel rims.
£7,500–9,500 *HAG*

1961 BSA A7 497cc, 190mm front brake, chrome mudguards and fuel tank, dual seat.
£1,400–1,700 *CBG*
This A7 has been uprated with a combination of Gold Star and A10 Road Rocket componants to produce an attractive special.

1966 BSA D7 Bantam De Luxe 172cc, unrestored condition, complete with faded cherry red metallic paintwork.
£350–450 *PS*
1966 was the final year of D7 production.

1972 BSA Firebird 650cc, street scrambler, American market model.
£4,000–5,000 *BKS*

1967 BSA A65 Thunderbolt 656cc, overhead valve unit construction twin cylinder.
£2,000–2,300 *PS*

1968 BSA Lightening 654cc, unit construction twin, 4-speed gearbox, BSA's answer to the Triumph Bonneville.
£2,000–2,500 *MWM*

1924 Connaught Sports 293cc, single cylinder
2-stroke, good condition.
£1,200–1,500 *PS*
*A rare and unusual vintage motorcycle, manufactured
by Bordersley Engineering Co, Birmingham.*

1966 Cotton Continental 370cc, single cylinder,
2-stroke Villiers Starmaker type engine, close ratio
gearbox, 12 volt generator.
£1,000–1,200 *PS*

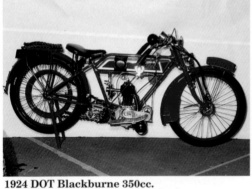

1924 DOT Blackburne 350cc.
£5,000–6,000 *DOT*
*This is the only DOT Blackburne known with a
350 side valve engine.*

1926 Douglas Model OC 596cc.
£6,500–7,500 *VER*
Douglas were well established by WWI.

1924 Coventry-Eagle Flying 8hp 998cc,
heavyweight 3-speed gearbox, bulb horn,
Swansea V5, VMCC dating certificate, black
paintwork, excellent condition.
£9,000–10,000 *BKS*

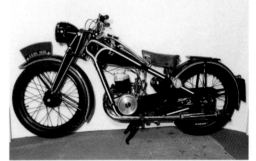

1936 CZ 175 174cc, single cylinder, 2-stroke, rigid
frame, blade forks, sprung saddle.
£2,000–2,700 *JCZ*

1951 DOT Model T 197cc, Villiers engine, restored,
good condition.
£2,000–2,500 *DOT*
*This motorcycle was unused for 34 years before
being restored.*

1951 Douglas Mark V 348cc, horizontally
opposed twin cylinder, torsion bar rear
suspension, leading link front fork, V5 log, good
condition, finished in polychromatic blue.
£1,500–2,000 *PS*

1902 Dreadnought 500cc, belt final drive, caliper brakes, rare veteran machine.
£12,000–14,000 *VMCC*

1951 Ducati 60 Sport 48cc, 4-stroke pull-rod engine, with 3 speeds, restored to original.
£1,000–1,200 *PC*

This model was the first Ducati complete motorcycle.

1959 Ducati Elite 204cc, single cylinder overhead camshaft, replaced saddle, 'jellymould' tank, restored but unmodified, V5 log.
£2,000–2,500 *PS*

1959 Ducati 125 Sport 124cc, overhead camshaft, restored to original specification, metallic blue/bronze paintwork.
£1,000–1,600 *MAY*

1974 Ducati 750 Sport, bevel V-twin, CEV switchgear, central axle fork, forward-mounted clip-ons, polished outer engine casings, dual seat, finished in yellow.
£5,000–5,500 *GLC*

This is one of the last Ducati 750 Sport motorcycles to be produced.

1975 Ducati Regolarita 124cc, 2-stroke, 6-speed piston port, with radial fin head.
£1,800–2,000 *PC*

Ex Pat Slinn 1975 ISDT mount, entered by British Ducati importers.

1980 Ducati 900SS 864cc, triple discs, 40mm carburettors, Conti silencers, Darmah type bottom end, Nippon denso/Bösch electrics, concours condition.
£4,000–5,000 *PC*

1981 Ducati 900SS, bevel V-twin, single saddle, wire wheels.
£4,500–5,000 *GLC*

This machine was built in the final year of production for the best-selling Ducati 900SS model which was painted in the famous black and gold.

1933 Francis-Barnett Cruiser 32 249cc, very good condition.
£800–900 *MWM*

This was the first model to carry the FB badge.

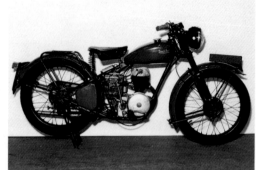

1950 Francis-Barnett Model 54 197cc, Villiers 6E engine, 3-speed foot operated gearbox, rigid frame, flywheel magneto ignition.
£400–425 *PS*

1959 Francis-Barnett Light Cruiser 174cc, 2-stroke, single cyclinder AMC engine, 4-speed gearbox, unit construction.
£800–1,000 *PC*

1910 FN 285cc, single cylinder, 2-speed gearbox, shaft final drive, acetylene headlamp, unsprung frame, running order.
£4,500–5,000 *BKS*

1948 FN Model XIII 450cc, rubber ring type front suspension, very good condition.
£1,500–1,750 *BLM*

1960 Gilera Extra 175cc, overhead valve, single cylinder with wet sump lubrication, 4-speed gearbox, telescopic forks, swinging arm rear suspension.
£1,700–1,800 *IMO*

1958 Gilera 300 Extra 304cc, overhead valve, parallel twin, unrestored, original condition.
Est. £1,100–1,300 *BKS*

1962 Gilera Jubilee 175cc, single cylinder, 4-stroke engine, very good condition.
£1,800–1,900 *IMO*
The Jubilee series was built to commemorate the Arcore factory's anniversary.

1963 Greeves Essex 246cc, Villiers 2T engine, good condition. £600–800 *BLM*

1963 Greeves 24 TES Trials 246cc, very good condition. £1,000–1,300 *BLM*

The best of the pre-1965 Greeves Trials.

1910 Haleson Steamer 206cc, very good condition. £12,000–15,000 *VMCC*

In 1903 Mr Hale of Bristol started design work to build a motorcycle – it was finally registered in January 1914, and remains the only example built.

1961 Greeves Sports Twin 249cc, Villiers 2T twin cylinder engine. £1,800–2,100 *GRA*

1974 Harley-Davidson SS350 344cc, overhead valve, twin port, single Aermacchi engine, electric start, double cradle frame. £1,700–1,900 *PC*

1967 Greeves Challenger 24 MX5 Challenger Motocrosser 246cc, 70 x 64mm, good condition. £2,000–2,100 *GRA*

1948 Harley-Davidson WLC 750cc, very good condition. £7,000–7,500 *BLM*

Approximately 20,000 WLCs were built for the Canadian forces.

1917 Harley Davidson 1000cc, all chain drive, foot and hand clutch, no front brakes, 2 independent rear brakes, originally olive green. £12,000–15,000 *FMC*

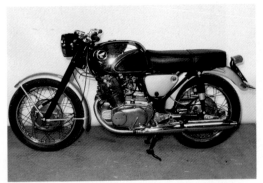

1965 Honda CB 72 247cc, air-cooled, 4-stroke engine, original condition, well maintained, mechanics in good order, V5 document.
£1,200–1,300 *BKS*

1977 Honda 400/4 398cc, carefully maintained, excellent condition, runs well, V5 document.
£1,400–1,600 *BKS*

1977 Honda GL1000 998cc, US import, excellent condition.
£1,500–2,000 *MWM*

1980 Honda CB400N 395cc, only 35,649km, V5 document, excellent condition.
£550–650 *PS*

1926 Humber 2¾hp Solo, flat tank 4-stroke, chain drive, good mechanical condition, V5 document.
Est. £3,250–3,500 *BKS*

1928 Humber 349cc, overhead valve, V5 document, good condition.
Est. £3,250–3,500 *BKS*

1927 Humber 349cc, totally original machine, stored from 1930–90, 1930 tax disc, tool kit, original supplier's transfers.
£2,800–3,000 *PVE*

1980 Honda ZR 49cc Monkey Bike, 4-stroke, good condition throughout.
£525–575 *BKS*

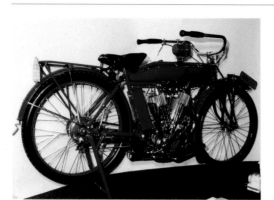

1911 Indian Regular 7hp,
very good condition.
£12,000–14,000 *VMCC*

1915 Indian Twin 680cc, very good condition.
£8,000–10,000 *PVE*

The last of the line to be designed by Oscar Hedstrom.

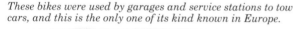

1940 Indian 45 Despatch Tow 750cc.
£22,000–24,000 *IMC*

These bikes were used by garages and service stations to tow cars, and this is the only one of its kind known in Europe.

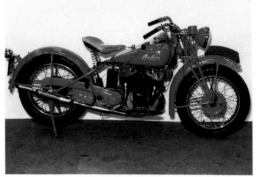

1941 Indian 741B Ex-Army V-Twin Side Valve Model 750cc, restored to civilian livery, V5 log, original green registration book, excellent condition.
£3,600–4,000 *PS*

1941 Indian Sports Scout 1200cc,
very good condition.
£10,000–12,000 *IMC*

1947 Indian Chief 1200cc, big bore V-twin engine, very good condition.
£10,000+ *IMC*

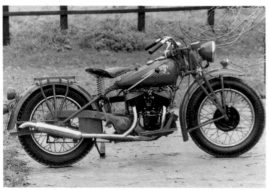

1947 Indian 741B Twin 500cc, civilian trim, concours condition.
£4,500–5,000 *BLM*

1941 Indian Chief 1200cc, V-twin, side valve.
£8,000–10,000 *IMC*

The 1940 and '41 Chiefs were identical in appearance except for different colour and tyre options.

1950 James Comet 98cc, Villiers engine,
2-speed gearbox, very good condition.
£200–250 *PS*

1959 James Cavalier 175cc, AMC engine,
4-speed gearbox, semi-rear enclosure, V5 log.
£380–420 *PS*

1960 Jawa Model 559 247cc, twin port,
single cylinder, 2-stroke.
£800–900 *JCZ*

1973 Jawa Model 360 344cc, very good condition.
£1,200–1,300 *JCZ*

*This was one of the last batch of classic styled
Jawas imported into the UK. Concessionaire at that
time was the famous motocross rider, Dave Bickers.*

1904 Kerry 500cc, direct belt drive,
very good condition.
£7,500–9,500 *FMC*

1978 Laverda Jota 1000cc, top speed of
140mph, well maintained, good condition.
£3,000–3,500 *BKS*

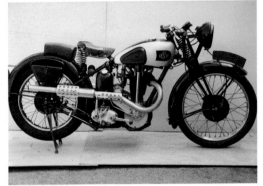

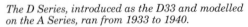

1936 Levis Model D 498cc, very good condition.
£1,500–1,800 *VER*

*The D Series, introduced as the D33 and modelled
on the A Series, ran from 1933 to 1940.*

1981 Laverda 500cc, double overhead camshaft,
parallel twin, very good condition.
£2,500–3,000 *GLC*

1925 Matador 350cc, engine designed by
Granville Bradshaw, restored to original condition.
£5,500–6,500 *PVE*

1980 Maico MD 250 WK 245cc, water-cooled,
2-stroke single.
£1,800–2,200 *MOC*

The only one known in the UK.

1951 Matchless G80S 497cc, very good condition.
£2,000–2,300 *BLM*

*One of the first Matchless roadsters to feature swinging
arm rear suspension.*

1941 Matchless G3L, overhead
valve engine, telescopic front forks,
ex-War Department, good condition.
£1,000–1,300 *BLM*

1953 Matchless G80 497cc, single cylinder,
overhead valve, fitted with 1949 engine,
V5 log, fair condition.
£1,300–1,500 *PS*

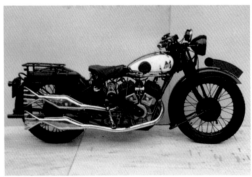

1931 Matchless Model X 1000cc,
very good condition.
£5,000–6,000 *VER*

One of the highly prized inter-war V-twin models.

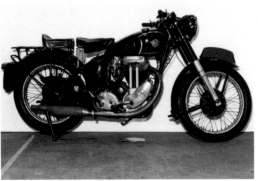

1951 Matchless G80 497cc, overhead valve single,
developed from the wartime G3L.
£1,700–2,000 *PS*

1964 Matchless G2 Monitor 248cc,
very good condition.
£700–1,000 *PS*

This is the smaller version of AMC's unit single.

1952 Moto Guzzi Airone Sport 246cc,
overhead valve, 4-stroke, single cylinder,
4-speed gearbox, sprung frame, telescopic forks.
£2,800–3,200 *S*

*Introduced in 1939 as a derivative of the PE,
the Airone remained in production until 1957.*

1960 Moto Guzzi Lodola 235cc, very good condition.
£1,000–1,200 *PVE*

*A recent import from Italy, this was the last bike to be
designed by Carlo Guzzi before his retirement.*

1960 MV Agusta 4T 150 Rapido Sport 149cc,
4-speed gearbox, 59.5 x 54mm, 10bhp at
7500rpm, good condition.
£1,800–2,000 *S*

*The original twin double-barrel silencers are not
fitted for ground clearance reasons.*

1975 Moto Guzzi Nuovo Falcone 499cc,
electric start, unit construction motor,
low mileage, immaculate original condition.
£2,500–3,000 *NLM*

1953 Moto Guzzi Zigolo 98cc, rotary valve
2-stroke single, good condition.
£1,000–1,100 *IMO*

From 1960 the engine was enlarged to 110cc.

1953 MV Agusta Pullman Turismo 123.5cc,
2-stroke, 3-speed gearbox, telescopic forks,
swinging arm rear, 15in (38cm) tyres.
£2,400–2,600 *S*

The Pullman was half motorcycle, half scooter.

1971 Moto Guzzi V7 Special 757cc, V-twin,
shaft drive, panniers, crashbars, de luxe
specification, very good condition.
£2,700–3,000 *IMO*

1969/70 MV Agusta 250B 247cc, overhead
valve twin, 19bhp, stepped seat, flat headlamp
rim, well maintained.
£1,500–1,700 *BKS*

1932 Norton 16H 490cc, side valve single, very good condition.
£2,200–2,400 *PS*

1934 Norton CJ 350cc, overhead camshaft, junior touring model, restored to original condition.
£10,000–11,000 *FMC*

1948 Norton Manx 30M 499cc, double overhead camshaft, 4-speed gearbox, 'Garden Gate', plunger rear suspension, very good condition.
£8,000–10,000 *VER*

1946 Norton Model 18 490cc, fitted with Brookland 'can' exhaust silencer, very good condition.
£2,000–2,250 *BLM*

1937 Norton Model 16H 490cc Military Motorcycle, fitted with canvas panniers and engine guard, V5 document, instruction manual, in running order, requires attention.
£1,800–2,000 *BKS*

1958 Norton International Model 30 499cc, very good condition.
£6,500–7,000 *BKS*
This machine was one of the last of a famous line.

1954 Norton Manx 40M 348cc, short stroke, double overhead camshaft, very good condition.
£9,500–10,000 *BKS*

1961 Norton Manx 30M 499cc, recently rebuilt, very good condition.
£16,000–18,000 *CRMC*

1963 Norton 650 Standard 646cc, slim-line twin carburettor Dominator, painted mudguards, painted chaincase, lower engine tune.
£2,200–2,500 *BLM*

1939 Panther Model 100 596cc, 4-speed posi-stop gearbox, fully restored, very good condition throughout.
£3,000–3,500 *BKS*

1972 Norton Commando 750S 745cc Street Scrambler, twin exhausts, V5 document, totally rebuilt, good condition throughout.
£3,000–3,500 *BKS*

1952 Panther Model 65 250cc, very good condition.
£1,600–1,800 *PM*

The Model 65 replaced the Model 60 from 1949 onwards.

1965 Panther Model 120 645cc,
very good condition.
£1,800–2,000 *PM*

1952 Panther M100 594cc, sloper big twin-port overhead valve single, very good condition.
£1,800–1,900 *PC*

1956 Panther Model 65 249cc, overhead valve, 4-speed gearbox, bore and stroke 60 x 88mm, very good condition.
£1,000–1,200 *BLM*

1975 Norton Interpol 829cc, full fairing, single seat, panniers, radio, calibrated Smiths' speedometer, excellent condition.
Est. £3,000–4,000 *S*

The Interpol police model was based on the 850 Commando MkIII.

DUCATI *(Italian 1946–)*
Desmo Profile

To Ducati enthusiasts around the world the name Ing Fabio Taglioni is one to be revered, for this gifted engineer can be considered the father of the company's legendary motorcycles. One of Italy's greatest motorcycle designers, he was the man responsible for the Desmo line of machines.

Taglioni joined Ducati as their head of design in May 1954 and was soon at work developing an overhead camshaft racing single. At the time a weakness of racing motorcycle engines was their valve springs, which were notoriously unreliable. This led to many manufacturers using the external hairpin type which were, at least, easily and quickly changed, although they still broke with monotonous regularity. Another problem caused by the use of springs to close the valves was that they allowed valve bounce at high rpm, robbing the engine of power.

Fabio Taglioni overcame the problems caused by the use of valve springs by dispensing with them completely and using a third camshaft to positively close the valves.

Thus, the engine could rev higher than one with conventional valve gear and produce more power.

Known as desmodromics, the principle of positively closing the valves was not a new one, even in the mid-1950s, but Taglioni was the first to develop it successfully for use in a motorcycle engine. At first, it was employed by Ducati for competition engines only, but in the 1960s production road-going bikes appeared with this feature in the shape of the 250 and 350 Mk3Ds in the spring of 1968, followed by a 450 the following year.

When the bevel drive V-twins came on the scene in the early 1970s it was not long before Taglioni used the same formula. This was tested with a racing version of the 750 to brilliant effect when Paul Smart and Bruno Spaggiari scored an impressive 1–2 in the inaugural Imola 200 in 1972.

By the end of the 1970s all Ducati's production models came with the Desmo system, a trend continued today in the street bikes and WSB (World Super Bike) racers.

1956 Ducati 125 TV 124cc, pushrod engine, Triumph-type headlamp nacelle, full loop frame, fully enclosed suspension, original, needing restoration.
£1,200–1,300 *PC*

1958 Ducati 175 Sport 174cc, twin barrel Silentium silencer, Dell'Orto carburettor, red and bronze finish.
£2,100–2,200 *PC*
The 175 model is now rare.

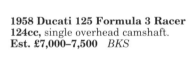

1958 Ducati 125 Formula 3 Racer 124cc, single overhead camshaft.
Est. £7,000–7,500 *BKS*

l. **1958 Ducati Elite 204cc,** overhead camshaft, single, restored, later rear light, otherwise original.
£3,000–3,500 *IVC*

1960 Ducati Type 48 Racing 48cc, fair condition, mechanical condition is unknown. **Est. £600–700** *BKS*

1959 Ducati 175 Motocross 174cc, FIII-type forks, full loop frame and specially brake tested motor, incorrect headlamp, toolboxes missing.
£3,800–3,900 *PC*

A very rare bike, one of only a handful built.

1961 Ducati Elite 204cc, overhead camshaft, all major original parts, including tin ware, battery and silencer missing, restoration project.
£1,000–1,200 *IVC*

1962 Ducati Daytona 248cc, overhead camshaft, short front mudguard, Borrani alloy rims, restored, very good condition.
£2,800–3,200 *IVC*

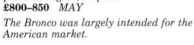

1962 Ducati Bronco 124cc, overhead valve.
£750–800 *PC*

American import as sold by Berliner Corporation of New Jersey.

1962 Ducati Bronco 124cc, overhead valve, pushrod engine, 4-speed.
£800–850 *MAY*

The Bronco was largely intended for the American market.

1964 Ducati 200GT 204cc, overhead camshaft, alloy wheel rims, non-standard, restored, good mechanical order.
£1,200–1,400 *MAY*

1963 Ducati 200 Elite 204cc, fully restored, needing battery and kickstart lever to complete.
£1,900–2,100 *PC*

1964 Ducati Elite 204cc, single cylinder, overhead camshaft, bevel drive.
£1,000–2,000 *CRC*

1966 Ducati Sebring 340cc.
£1,200–1,300 *PC*

Ex-American market machine imported by Bill Hannah.

1966 Ducati Mach I 248cc, standard except rev counter, alloy rims, Dell'Orto SS129D carburettor, red and silver finish, pristine example.
£3,000–3,500 *PC*

1966 Ducati Cadet 100 94cc, fan-cooled, 2-stroke.
£800–1,000 *PC*

One of a large range of small capacity 2-stroke models offered by Ducati during much of the 1960s.

1966 Ducati Mach I 248cc, overhead camshaft, 5-speed, Dell'Orto SS129D carburettor, rearsets, clip-ons, Veglia racing tacho, curved kickstart lever, good condition.
£3,250–3,750 *IVC*

1968 Ducati 250 MkIII 248cc, overhead camshaft, rare twin filler cap model, unrestored.
£1,750–2,000 *IVC*

1971 Ducati 450 R/T Desmo 436cc.
£1,800–2,300 *IVC*

Off-road model created for the American market, rare in Europe.

1974 Ducati 250 Desmo Disc 248cc, 35mm Ceriani forks, Brembo disc front brake, alloy rims, clip-ons, non-standard silencer, yellow and black finish.
£2,400–2,800 *PC*

1974 Ducati 750SS 748cc.
£15,000–16,000 *PC*

Actual bike ridden by Mick James to win 1974 500kms race, entrant Mick Walker Motorcycles. Now in road trim.

1972 Ducati 250 Road 248cc.
£1,000–1,200 *PC*

Spanish built model from Mototrans, Barcelona factory. Originally sold to USA importer Berliner of New Jersey, subsequently exported to Britain in early 1980s.

1974 Ducati 450 Scrambler 436cc.
£1,900–2,100 *PC*

Last of the Scrambler models with double-sided front brake.

1974 Ducati Desmo 350cc.
£3,000–3,500 *IVC*

Today one of the most sought-after Ducati models.

1977 Ducati 350 Sport Desmo 349cc, Desmo overhead camshaft parallel twin.
£1,600–1,700 *PC*

1978 Ducati Sport Desmo 500cc.
£1,000–1,500 *IVC*

A vastly under-rated motorcycle, with good looks and plenty of power.

1979 Ducati 900 Mike Hailwood Replica (MHR) 864cc, V-twin Speedline wheels, Conti silencers, 40mm Dell'Orto carburettors, gold line Brembo brakes, No. 32 in the series.
£4,000–5,000 *IVC*

1979 Ducati GTV 350 349cc, chain driven overhead camshaft engine, 5-speed, cast alloy wheels, triple disc brakes, non-standard silencers.
£750–1,000 *MAY*

1982 Ducati Pantah 600SSL 583cc, Conti 2-into-2 exhaust system.
£2,500–2,700 *IVC*

1982 Ducati Pantah 600SL 583cc, original except 2 into one Conti exhaust and Forcella Italia front forks.
£2,000–2,300 *PC*

ESO
(Czechoslovakian 1949–62)

1960 Eso Speedway 499cc, overhead valve.
£2,500–3,000 *PC*
Ridden by world champion Peter Collins.

EXCELSIOR
(British 1886–1964)

1923 Excelsior 147cc, 2-stroke engine, belt final drive.
Est. £2,000–2,400 *S*

1935 Excelsior Lightweight 149cc.
Est. £500–550 *BKS*

1937 Excelsior Manxman 249cc, overhead camshaft.
£5,800–6,200 *BKS*
The Excelsior Manxman never won a TT race outright, but this model featuring the powerful overhead camshaft engine unit nevertheless earned a well-deserved reputation for race reliability. The 250cc variant could be ordered as a fast sports road model or in full race trim.

GILERA *(Italian 1909–93)*

Gilera was one of the truly great names in motorcycling, its history spanning much of the twentieth century.

The famous Arcore marque was founded by Giuseppe Gilera, who was born in December 1887, in a small village near Milan.

Brought up in a working-class family, even as a schoolboy the young Giuseppe was fascinated by all forms of mechanised transport, which were then in their infant stage of development; he went to work in the Bianchi factory in Milan at the age of 15. Displaying an aptitude far above his age and upbringing, Gilera soon moved on to work as a mechanic with the Italian branch of the Swiss Moto Reve concern. Then after a spell in Geneva with an engineering firm, he returned to Italy in 1908. The following year he began to build his own bikes, the first being a 317cc single with IOE (inlet over exhaust). Like many other fledgling manufacturers of the era, Gilera soon went racing, his first victory coming at Cremona in 1912.

During WWI Gilera turned his hand to building bicycles for the Italian army. Following the end of hostilities there was a massive demand for motorcycles in Italy, but it was not until 1920 that Gilera was able to capitalise on this, after moving out of Milan to a much larger factory at Arcore.

Besides its roadsters Gilera, throughout the 1920s, gained considerable success in long distance trials – thanks in no small part to the exploits of younger brother Luigi, who won many 'Golds' mainly with sidecars.

The big breakthrough in motorcycle sport came in late 1937 following the purchase of the 4 cylinder Rondine racing and record breaker, and Gilera were European champions in 1939. Then came WWII and Gilera, like Norton, built military bikes rather than racers.

Post-war the Arcore factory was soon working flat out. In racing, Gilera won four 500cc (1952, 1953, 1955 and 1957) and one 350cc (1957) world titles. After they retired at the end of 1957 a series of world records were set at Monza, most notably the classic hour (McIntyre).

In the 1960s sales dropped alarmingly, then came a series of crippling strikes. By 1969 the factory was all but bankrupt, Piaggio, the makers of the Vespa scooter, gained control. Then a rebirth followed during the 1970s and 1980s, but this did not last and then on the eve of the 1993 Milan show Piaggio pulled the plug and Gilera was no more.

1948 Gilera Saturno Sport 498cc.
£5,000–5,500 *IVC*

Italy's equivalent of the English BSA Gold Star.

1950 Gilera Saturno 498cc, overhead valve, unrestored.
£2,000–3,500 *PC*

Designed in the late 1930s, the Saturno did not enter full production until after WWII. The original version shown here was built from 1946 until 1950. It had girder forks and a crude form of rear springing.

1956 Gilera 175 Sport 174cc, overhead valve, original example.
£1,500–1,600 *PC*

UK imports of Gilera were handled during the late 1950s and early 1960s by London-based dealers, Pride and Clarke.

1957 Gilera 175 Twin 174cc, double overhead camshaft.
£18,000–22,000 *PC*

Genuine ex-works racing model, built for long distance events such as the Giro d'Italia (Tour of Italy) and Milano-Taranto. Only four such machines were made.

1957 Gilera Rosso 175cc, non-standard.
£1,500–1,600 *IMO*

1958 Gilera Saturno 498cc, overhead valve,
swinging arm rear suspension, telescopic forks.
£4,500–5,000 *PC*

c1958 Gilera Saturno 498cc Racer,
converted roadster.
£3,400–3,600 *PC*

1959 Gilera Rossa Extra 174cc, overhead valve,
full width brake hubs, red and white paintwork,
concours condition.
£1,800–1,900 *PC*

1959 Gilera 175 Rossa Extra 174cc, parallel
valve pushrod engine, original, unrestored.
£750–1,100 *IVC*

1962 Gilera B300 304cc, overhead valve twin,
restored, silencers and several small parts missing.
£1,200–1,300 *PC*

**1965 Gilera 124 Regolarita Competizione
124cc,** overhead valve.
£2,500–2,600 *PC*

*A limited number of genuine enduro Gileras were
built in the mid- to late 1960s. These were available
in 124 and 175cc engine sizes. They were gold
medal winners in the gruelling ISDT (International
Six Days Trial).*

1974 Gilera RS50 Touring 49cc,
2-stroke, excellent original condition.
£350–450 *MR*

r. **1977 Gilera TG1 124cc,** single cylinder,
2-stroke, alloy head and barrel, 5-speed,
cast alloy wheels, disc front brake.
£350–400 *PC*

GREEVES *(British 1952–78)*

r. **c1972 Greeves Pathfinder 170cc,** with Puch engine. **Est. £100–150** *BKS*

The Austrian Puch-engined model was the last of the Greeves trials bikes.

c1973 Greeves Griffon 380cc. £800–1,000 *BKS*

GRIFFON
(French 1902–late 1920s)

1904 Griffon MV 2¾hp. £6,000–8,000 *VMCC*

HARLEY-DAVIDSON
(American 1903–)

1969 Harley-Davidson KR750 Racer 741cc, side valve, 69.77 x 96.84mm, 45° V-twin. **£25,000–30,000** *PC*

Raced by Cal Rayborn at Daytona in 1969.

l. **1976 Harley-Davidson XR750 748cc,** flat track racer, alloy cylinder, pristine condition. **£11,000–12,000** *PC*

1972 Harley-Davidson XLH Sportster 998cc, V-twin. **£5,800–6,200** *BKS*

HESKETH
(British 1981–)

1982 Hesketh V1000 1000cc, overhead camshaft, V-twin. **£5,000–6,000** *S*

HONDA
(Japanese 1946–)

1962 Honda Benly C92 124cc, overhead camshaft twin.
Est. £500–600 *BKS*
Touring version of the Benly.

1962 Honda Benly C92 125cc.
Est. £450–550 *BKS*

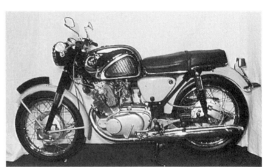

1963 Honda CB72 247cc Sports, standard specification, original blue saddle, seamed silencers.
£1,800–2,000 *PC*

1966 Honda CB450 445cc.
Est. £2,200–2,500 *BKS*

1967 Honda CB77 305cc.
£550–650 *BKS*
This is now one of the most desirable of early Japanese classics.

1967 Honda 90 Sports 90cc.
Est. £380–420 *BKS*

1969 Honda CB750 736cc.
£4,000–4,500 *S*

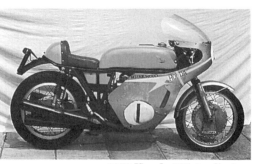

c1970 Honda 500 4 cylinder Hailwood Replica.
£2,500–3,000 *IVC*
A unique machine in road trim.

1973 Honda SL125 Trail 122cc, good example.
£1,400–1,800 *S*

1974 Honda SL125 Single Cylinder Trail Bike 122cc, requires attention.
£120–180 *PS*

One of Honda's earliest trail bikes.

l. **1975 Honda CB175 174cc.**
£500–550 *BKS*

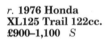

r. **1976 Honda XL125 Trail 122cc.**
£900–1,100 *S*

1976 Honda CB750 K6 736cc.
£2,000–2,250 *BKS*

1977 Honda Gold Wing GL1000 Executive 998cc.
Est. £8,000–10,000 *BKS*

The Executive was a limited edition of the GL1000 of which only 50 were made to commemorate the Queen's Jubilee. This example is unregistered and has only delivery mileage.

1978 Honda Gold Wing GL 1000cc, 4 cylinder horizontally opposed engine.
£1,000–1,500 *MR*

HUMBER
(British 1900–30)

1928 Humber 349cc, overhead valve.
Est. £3,400–3,800 *BKS*

The original Humber works made penny-farthing bicycles, then through a series of disasters and financial rearrangements the factory settled at Coventry and began the serious business of manufacturing motorcycles. Always innovative, by the mid- to late 1920s the motorcycle side was beginning to take second place to Humber's car production, with the 350 range being their main outlet.

1983 Honda CB 1100R Production Racer 1100cc, 125hp, 4 cylinders, double overhead camshaft.
£3,500–4,500 *CRC*

INDIAN
(American 1901, British 1951–53)

Scout and Chief 1920–39 Profile

Indian's chief designer was Charles B. Franklin. His greatest designs were the intermediate Scout and massive Chief, both side valve V-twins.

The 37 cubic inch (600cc) Scout appeared in late 1919 ready for the 1920 season and was an instant hit. Scouts were renowned for their staying power – witness the factory advertising slogan 'You can't wear out an Indian Scout'. This was no idle boast, for a Scout set a new 24-hour road record in 1920, covering 1,114 miles over a closed course in Australia. To set this in perspective the previous record was not only 250 miles shorter, but set by a machine with almost twice the capacity!

Following quickly after the Scout came Franklin's next design, the 61 cubic inch (1000cc) Chief in 1922. This too was both a sales and reliability success. A year later the Chief was joined by the even larger 74 cubic inch 1200cc Big Chief.

Strangely it was the Scout which managed to grab the really big headlines, even though, in engine capacity, it was the smallest of the Indian V-twins of the era. For example, a Scout broke both the Canada – Mexico and transcontinental records in 1923, records previously set by the Excelsior V-twin and Henderson 4 cylinder models.

Only detail model changes were made to the Chief between 1924 and 1929, the most important being the addition of a front brake for 1928, a feature also incorporated into the Scout range. The Scout saw more changes, with a 45 cubic inch version market alongside the original 37 cubic inch model from 1927. Eventually from 1929 onwards only the larger Scout was offered.

The Indian marque was bought by E. Paul du Pont in 1930. A smaller version of the Scout (31 cubic inches) made its debut in 1932, whilst in 1933 dry sump lubrication was adopted for all the Indian V-twins. With rivals Harley-Davidson not opting to use dry sump lubrication until 1937, Indian stole a march on the competition. The next step was the 45 cubic inch Sport Scout in 1934. This had a more racy appearance and choice of 3 or 4 speeds (the latter from 1937 onwards). In standard trim it had a maximum speed of 80–85mph, and when tuned could exceed 100mph. Also the Sport Scout dispensed with the famous Indian helical geared primary drive. Likewise from this period onwards the Chief and Standard Scout had also switched to primary drive by means of a chain running in a cast alloy oil bath – a four-row chain for the Chief and a three-row component for the smaller Vs. This didn't meet the approval of Indian enthusiasts at the time, but where it counted, in service, the chain primary drive proved long-lasting.

For 1935 the Chief was available with the option of the 'Y' engine, which featured larger cylinder cooling fins and alloy cylinder heads with larger fins. The year was also the last one in which Indian enjoyed a clear styling advantage over their Harley rivals.

In 1936, battery/coil ignition was standardised, but the classic magneto remained an optional extra. Nickel-plated cylinders were another innovation introduced at this time.

It is also worth mentioning the so-called 'Trench' head on Chiefs. If a head was held for inspection, showing inside, a V-shaped trench can be seen to separate the valve area from the combustion turbulance.

For 1938 high performance versions of the Scout and Chief were called Daytona in recognition of Ed Kretz's victory in the 1937 Daytona 200 race. Engineering changes that year were aimed at cooler running, with extra cylinder/head finery being added on the Sport Scout and Chief. There was also a new oil pump of increased capacity, plus a new gear-driven return pump. New colour scheme and more chrome plate arrived for 1939, but technical changes were virtually non-existent.

With the advent of the 1940s came war rather than peace. Indian found themselves building bikes for the army and after the conflict was over they never again challenged Harley-Davidson for the number one spot as they had in the pre-war days.

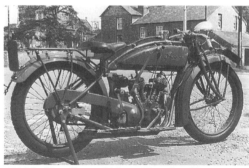

1921 Indian Scout 596cc, side valve, V-twin, 37 cu in.
£8,000–9,000 *PC*

1923 Indian Big Chief 1200cc.
£8,000–9,000 *BKS*
The earliest Big Chief model known to exist in UK.

1924 Indian Scout 596cc.
£5,500–6,500 *BKS*

c1925 Indian Scout 600cc.
£8,000–9,000 *AtMC*

> **Miller's is a price GUIDE not a price LIST**

l. **c1940 Indian 741B 500cc.**
£2,300–2,800 *BKS*

JAMES
(British 1902–64)

1923 James 3hp.
£1,800–2,200 *BKS*

1925 James Flat Tank 3hp.
£2,500–3,000 *BLM*

1960 James Captain L20 199cc,
AMC engine.
Est. £400–600 *S*

1962 James L15A Flying Cadet 149cc,
2-stroke, AMC engine.
£250–500 *CRC*

JAWA
(Czechoslovakian 1929–)

1957 Jawa Type 356 175cc, twin port,
single cylinder, 2-stroke engine.
Est. £750–950 *S*

1963 Jawa 579/01 247cc.
£1,000–1,200 *PC*
This is similar to Model 575, early competition model.

1965 Jawa Twin Port Motocross Type 768,
completely rebuilt.
£2,500–3,000 *JCZ*

1969 Jawa Model 654 402cc.
£1,200–1,400 *PC*

*Motorcross conversion of ISDT bike,
the famous 'banana' frame model.*

KAWASAKI
(Japanese 1962–)

1968 Kawasaki Samurai 247cc, disc valve,
2-stroke twin.
Est. £2,100–2,500 *BKS*

*This machine has been restored to show standard
having previously been awarded 1988 Best
Japanese Machine at the Classic Bike Show at
Stafford.*

1974 Kawasaki H2B 748cc, 3 cylinder, 2-stroke.
£2,500–2,800 *CRC*

*Now very rare, the infamous H2B 750 only
obtained 12mpg if ridden hard.*

1978 Kawasaki KH250 249.5cc, 3 cylinders,
2-stroke, new and un-used.
£1,500–2,500 *CRC*

1979 Kawasaki KH250 B4 249.5cc, 3 cylinders,
2-stroke, with disc front brake, fair condition.
£600–700 *MAY*

LAVERDA *(Italian 1949–)*

1972 Laverda 750SF 743.9cc, twin overhead camshaft, original condition.
£1,600–2,000 *IVC*

1976 Laverda SFC 750cc, original condition.
Est. **£10,000–14,000** *S*

1980 Laverda Formula 500 Production Racer 497cc, overhead camshaft, non-standard Oscam wheels and exhaust.
£3,400–3,700 *IVC*

The Formula 500 was developed from the Alpino roadster. A series of races for these machines were successfully organised during the late 1970s and carried through into the early 1980s in Italy.

1981 Laverda Jota 1000cc, later model with half-fairing.
Est. **£3,600–3,800** *BKS*

LEVIS *(British 1911–39)*

c1914 Levis, two-stroke.
£2,500–3,000 *AtMC*

1983 Laverda Mirage Sport 1200cc, Koni rear shock absorbers, silver paintwork.
Est. **£2,300–3,300** *S*

MAGNAT
(French 1906– late '50s)

c1924 Magnat Debon 250cc, air-cooled inclined single cylinder engine with magneto ignition, Gurtner carburettor, 2-speed hand change gearbox, original red and black livery.
£720–800 *BKS*

1938 Levis SV Trials 346cc, black and silver finish, sound condition.
Est. **£1,200–1,800** *S*

Introduced for the 1938/39 model season, this was the only side-valve machine produced by Levis.

MAICO *(German 1926–)*

Maico is acknowledged as one of the most famous names in the field of off-road sport, but it is also well respected for its range of highly original road-going motorcycles, scooters and even cars. The marque's history can be traced to 1926 in Poltringen, near Stuttgart. It was not until 1931 that the Maico story had its first real two-wheel connection, when the two young sons of the founder began building bicycles in a small workshop at the rear of the factory.

The result was that Otto and Wilhelm Maisch built a motorcycle in 1935 designated MP120. This was a neat looking roadster using a bought-in Ilo two-stroke engine which all Maico motorcycles used prior to 1939. In 1939 the company introduced the Maico-Sachsonette. It was an autocycle with a 50cc Sachs motor. The war took its toll on Maico, but after much work the factory was totally rebuilt and the enterprise relaunched in 1947. A year later the company's first post-war machine was not only in production, but being offered for sale. This was the M125, which at last fulfilled the Maisch brothers'

dream of an all-Maico motorcycle, which was followed by the M150.

Later a more innovative design was commissioned. This was the famous Mobil, one of the stranger devices created by the post-war German industry. It was actually a very useful scooter, but with excellent carrying capacity and good roadholding.

The success of the M125/150 and Mobil secured Maico's future. More creations followed including: M151, M175, M200 and the twin cylinder Taifun (Typhoon), the latter built in 350 and 400cc engine sizes. There was also the Maicoletta de luxe scooter.

Not content with purely roadgoing bikes and scooters Maico became involved with long distance trials winning a hatful of medals in events, including the ISDT. The next step was into off-road racing and motocross and in these events Maico won many championships from the late 1950s right through to the early 1980s. They were even involved in road racing, with riders such as Kent Anderson, Dieter Braun and Chas Mortimer.

1955 Maico Taifun 348cc, streamlined front mudguard, 'bath-tub' rear enclosure.
£2,000–2,500 *PC*

1958 Maico Blizzard 247cc, Earles-type front brakes, concours condition.
£1,700–1,800 *PC*

r. **1977 Maico GS400 386cc.**
£900–1,100 *PC*

Enduro version of championship winning Maico motocrosser.

1956 Maico M175 Supersport 174cc, single cylinder, piston port induction, iron cylinder and alloy head, concours condition.
£1,700–1,800 *PC*

1967 Maico MD125 Sport 123.5cc, rotary valve 2-stroke, alloy cylinder and reborable iron liner.
£1,500–1,600 *PC*

MATCHLESS
(British 1901–69, revived 1987)

1930 Matchless Silver Arrow 398cc, side valve,
V-twin engine, original unrestored condition.
Est. £4,000–5,000 *S*

c1950 Matchless G3LS Special 347cc,
racing conversion.
£950–1,000 *BKS*

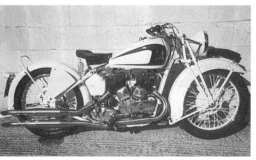

1937 Matchless Model X 1000cc, v-twin,
excellent condition.
£5,500–6,000 *AT*

1952 Matchless Spring Twin G9 498cc, single
sided brakes, 'jampot' rear shock absorbers, short
stubby megaphone silencer.
£2,000–2,500 *BLM*

*These are the characteristics of the early models of
the Matchless (and AJS) 500 twins.*

l. **1950 Matchless
G3L 347cc.
£2,500–2,750** *BKS*

*This machine was
manufactured in
1950 when the
motorcycle industry
was still in the grips
of post-war austerity.
The 'L' denotes the
fitting of telescopic
front forks.*

1953 Matchless G9 Spring Twin 498cc,
touring twin with megaphone silencers and
'jampot' rear shock absorbers.
£2,750–3,000 *BLM*

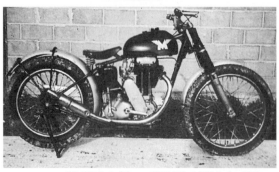

1946 Matchless G80 Rigid Trials 497cc.
£2,000–2,500 *BLM*

1953 Matchless G80S 497cc, solid reliable workhorse.
£2,000–2,250 *BLM*

1954 Matchless G9 498cc, modified to Enduro specification.
£1,800–2,000 *S*

r. **1955 Matchless G32 Competition 348cc,** good original order.
£2,250–2,500 *BKS*

1955 Matchless G9 Clubman 498cc, unique AMC overhead valve twin cylinder, with centre main bearing.
£2,500–3,000 *BLM*

1956 Matchless G9 498cc, overhead valve twin, fully restored.
£2,000–2,250 *BKS*

1956 Matchless G80 498cc.
£2,800–3,000 *BKS*

1957 Matchless G80 Competition 498cc, single cylinder, alloy engine.
£2,500–3,500 *CRC*

r. **1958 Matchless G3LS 348cc,** overhead valve single, 4-speed gearbox, swinging arm rear suspension, telescopic forks, full width hubs, dual seat.
£2,000–2,500 *BLM*

c1958 Matchless G80 Metisse APP 500cc Motocrosser, excellent condition.
£4,000–5,000   *SW*

1958 Matchless G11 600cc, twin engine, original condition.
£2,000–2,250   *AT*

1959 Matchless G12 646cc.
£3,000–3,300   *BLM*

Launched in late 1958, the G12 and its AJS counterpart, the Model 31, were developed from the earlier G11/Model 30 with its 593cc capacity.

1961 Matchless G3C 348cc, single cylinder, heavyweight.
£1,700–2,500   *CRC*

1961 Matchless G3 347cc, overhead valve, single cylinder.
£500–550   *PS*

This model was never as popular or respected as its heavyweight brother. Sold under both the Matchless and AJS labels it featured a pushrod unit construction engine. Also made in 250cc version.

1966 Matchless G50 Rickman Metisse Racer 496cc, overhead camshaft, single cyinder.
Est. £10,500–11,000   *BKS*

r. **c1962 Matchless CSR G12 646cc.**
£4,500–5,000   *AtMC*

MMC (British 1898–)

1902 MMC 411cc.
£5,750–6,000 *S*

MOTOBECANE
(French 1923–)

1933 Motobecane B33A 250cc, good order throughout.
Est. £2,500–2,800 *BKS*

MOTOBI (Italian 1949–76)

Founded by one of the Benelli brothers, Giuseppe Benelli, in 1949, the Motobi concern earned an enviable reputation for the quality of their products and their innovative design features, the most notable of which was the streamlined, egg-like shape of their power units. Initially production was concentrated on two-stroke powerplants, but in 1956 Giuseppe entered the 4-stroke field with a pair of overhead valve singles in 125 and 175cc capacities. These engines would later increase in capacity to 250cc and led to a number of racing machines that met with considerable success.

1960 Motobi Catria Turismo 174cc, overhead valve, original condition, running order.
£600–800 *IVC*

c1958 Motobi Formula 3 249cc Racing.
Est. £2,800–3,600 *S*

1963 Motobi Catria Sport 174cc, overhead valve, good original condition.
£1,200–1,500 *IVC*

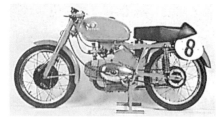

c1960 Motobi Sprint 175cc, overhead valve, good condition.
£1,600–1,800 *BKS*

1960 Motobi Sprite 124cc, overhead valve.
£600–1,200 *NLM*

The egg-shape unit construction engine was a distinctive feature of Giuseppe Benelli's break-away Motobi marque for much of its existence.

r. **1970 Motobi Tornado 650cc.**
£900–1,200 *IVC*

The Tornado was Italy's answer to the British Triumph Bonneville.

MOTO GUZZI
(Italian 1921–)

The early history of Moto Guzzi began when three young men serving in the Italian Air Arm during WWI dreamed of building their own motorcycle. When the war ended the two surviving members, Giorgio Parodi and Carlo Guzzi, set up the Moto Guzzi company in 1921 with financial backing from Parodi's family, an established dynasty of ship owners from the port of Genoa.

From a starting point of 10 employees in 1921, including the two partners, Moto Guzzi grew to become Italy's largest and most famous factory employing hundreds by the mid-1930s.

From the company's entry into racing in its earliest days until its withdrawal in 1957, it favoured a horizontal single cylinder engine format, and with this basic design Guzzi machines and riders won ten TTs and eight World Championships.

Although Moto Guzzi achieved numerous Continental successes in its early days it was not until 1935, when Stanley Woods won both the Lightweight and Senior TTs that Guzzi's efforts were crowned with truly international acclaim. Other notable pre-war victories came in the 1937 Lightweight TT and the epic defeat of the mighty DKWs in the 1939 German Grand Prix.

Remaining faithful to the horizontal single cylinder, Guzzi largely dominated the post-war 250cc class from 1947 until 1953. Then the Mandello del Lario company enlarged the engine capacity, entered the 350cc class and astounded the racing fraternity by winning the world title at its first attempt.

Guzzi will always be remembered for its amazing versatility in design, for in addition to the famous singles it produced machines with V-twin, across-the-frame 3 cylinders, in-line 4 cylinders and even a V8 engine!

After financial crisis in the 1960s the company was resurrected in the 1970s with the backing of the Argentinian industrialist De Tomaso and the success of its range of V-twin touring and sports bikes. Descendants of these machines still form the cornerstone of Guzzi's current range of motorcycles.

1949 Moto Guzzi Moto Legerra 65cc, rotary valve 2-stroke engine, 3 speeds, blade-type forks, sprung saddle.
£1,000–1,100   *PC*

1952 Moto Guzzi Zigolo 98cc, 2-stroke single cylinder.
£60–70   *PS*

1955 Moto Guzzi Falcone 499cc.
Est. £4,500–4,800   *BKS*

Introduced in 1950 as the successor to the GTW, the Falcone saw production in civilian and military guise and continued to be listed until 1976. The Falcone name, first used right at the start of Moto Guzzi production in 1921, was to endure on a succession of well-engineered singles until the 1970s.

1956 Moto Guzzi Falcone Sport 499cc, overhead valve horizontal single, restored.
£6,000–7,000   *IVC*

r. **1961 Moto Guzzi Lodola GT 235cc,** overhead valve, concours condition.
£1,800–2,000   *PVE*

This model was the last machine designed by Carlo Guzzi before his retirement.

1974 Moto Guzzi 750S3 748cc, V-twin transverse engine, good condition.
£2,500–3,000 *BKS*

1975 Moto Guzzi Nuovo Falcone Polizia 499cc, electric start engine, double-barrel silencer, screen and leg shields.
£1,500–2,000 *NLM*

MOTO MORINI
(Italian 1937–)

1955 Moto Morini 175 Tresette GT 174cc.
£1,300–1,700 *BKS*

This was the touring version of Morini's popular overhead valve single.

1980 Moto Guzzi V50 Series II 490cc, unrestored.
£400–500 *MR*

1958 Moto Morini 175 Gran Turismo, overhead valve.
£1,750–2,000 *IVC*

Touring version of the Settebello production racer.

1958 Moto Morini Tresette Sprint 175cc, overhead valve, original condition.
£900–1,200 *IVC*

1959 Moto Morini 175 Settebello 174cc, Clubman's racer, specially tuned and brake-tested engine, close ratio gears.
£750–850 *BKS*

1968 Moto Morini Corsaro 124cc, overhead valve, unit construction, full width hubs, clip-on handlebars, wet sump lubrication.
£850–950 *NLM*

1962 Moto Morini Tresette Sprint 174cc, full width hubs, alloy rims, clip-on handlebars, rare.
£1,500–1,800 *NLM*

1978 Moto Morini 3½ Sport, V-twin, cast alloy wheels, disc front brake, 6-speed gearbox.
£1,000–1,500 *IVC*

1981 Moto Morini 250 2C 249cc, V-twin, Heron combustion chambers and parallel valves, 6-speed gearbox.
£1,200–1,300 *NLM*

1980 Moto Morini 500 Sport 478.6cc, V-twin, immaculate, original condition.
£1,750–2,500 *IVC*

MÜNCH *(Germany 1966–)*

1971 Münch Mammoth 1177cc Solo.
£14,000–15,000 *BKS*

Friedl Münch's fantastic Mammoth was conceived as a super-bike in the 1960s and powered by an air-cooled NSU 4 cylinder power unit, suitably modified to fit in a Friedl designed frame inspired by Norton's Featherbed.

1984 Moto Morini 350 Kanguro 344cc, V-twin trail model, hi-level exhaust, rear carrier, original condition.
£800–1,100 *IVC*

MV AGUSTA *(Italian 1945–78)*
The Agusta Dynasty – Profile

No other marque has quite the same charisma as MV Agusta and today even its most basic models are in demand.

The marque history began in 1907 when a wealthy Italian named Giovanni Agusta decided to build his own aircraft, less than four years after the Wright brothers' first flight.

Born in the northern town of Parma in 1879, Giovanni Agusta could be described as one of Italy's aviation pioneers alongside men such as Pensuti, Caproni and Anzani. The first successful flight of his bi-plane, Ag 1, took place in the same year as construction had begun. In 1911 he designed a parachute, the prototype for others to follow.

After service in Libya as a government volunteer, he formed Construzioni Aeronautiche Giovanni Agusta in 1920 and moved to Cassina Costa, Gallerate, just outside Milan, three years later. The company continued to expand and 1927 saw the maiden flight of the Ag 2 monoplane, one of the first purpose built sports planes constructed in Italy. Later that year Giovanni Agusta died at only 48 years of age. The business then passed to his wife, Giuseppina Turretta Agusta. She and Giovanni had four sons, Vincenzo, Mario, Corrado and Domenico, the eldest, who soon proved to have a natural flair for commercial life. Not only did the young Domenico, then 21 years old, weather this storm but he was to remain head of the Agusta empire until his own death many years later in 1971.

Throughout the 1930s the company prospered on repairs and sub-contract work in the civil aviation industry but continued to produce their own aircraft, notably the Ag B6 of 1936, a four-seat single-engined light plane. Then came a period of military contracts, both for component parts and sub-contracting complete aircraft – Agusta building examples of the Breda Ba88 attack plane and the Fiat BR20 bomber.

Like other Italian aviation companies, Agusta's real problems began as the war ended. For under the terms of surrender they were not allowed to produce any aviation products. However, Domenico Agusta had seen this coming and as early as 1943 had made a move to put his production facilities to a different use. He selected motorcycles because there would be a ready market for an economical means of transport in the aftermath of war.

Their first effort gave no hint of the famous racing models to come, being a simple 98cc, single cylinder, 2-stroke. This was in 1945 and by 1947 the range had spread to a 125cc, 2-stroke and a 250 4-stroke, the latter an overhead valve, showing British influence. Again 2-strokes paved the way when Agusta entered racing in the late 1940s, which was soon followed by a myriad of 4-strokes from the early 1950s onwards.

Aviation was always important to Agusta and following a relaxation in the rules they signed an agreement in 1952 to manufacture the American Bell helicopters.

Ultimately the very success of the helicopter venture was to signal the end of MV Agusta the bike manufacturer. This not only resulted from Domenico's death in 1971, but because the Italian government saw Agusta primarily as a defence contractor and to protect its interests took a 51% shareholding in 1973 at a time when the Agusta group was headed by Corrado, the youngest of the four brothers. Developing aircraft is a long-term task requiring millions and so motorcycle production ceased. The final MV roadsters were built in 1978.

1949 MV Agusta 123.5cc Ex-Works Racing Motorcycle, extremely rare.
Est. £4,000–5,000 *BKS*

1950 MV Agusta Turismo E Lusso (TEL) 123.5cc, single cylinder piston port 2-stroke, 4-speed gearbox, fully sprung frame with girder front forks.
Est. £2,000–2,500 *S*

Miller's is a price
GUIDE not a price LIST

l. **1950 MV Agusta 123.5cc Ex-Works Racing Motorcycle,** rare and unusual.
Est. £4,000–5,000 *BKS*

1956 MV Agusta 175CSS Squalo (Shark) 172cc Racing Motorcycle, based on the single camshaft CS roadster, modified frame, Earles forks, external mounted magneto.
£4,200–4,700 *S*

1956 MV Agusta 175CS Disco Volante (Flying Saucer) 172.4cc, single overhead camshaft, 11bhp at 6700rpm, 4-speed gearbox, telescopic front forks and alloy rims.
Est. £2,600–3,200 *BKS*

1956 MV Agusta 174cc Squalo Production Racer, an original engine, replica frame, excellent condition.
£3,500–4,000 *S*

1956 MV Agusta 150 Turismo 149cc, overhead valve, 4-speed gearbox.
£600–800 *IVC*

1956 MV Agusta 175 CSTL 172.3cc, single overhead camshaft.
£1,800–2,200 *S*

This machine is the touring version of MV's famous 175 model range.

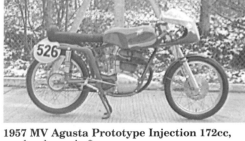

1957 MV Agusta Prototype Injection 172cc, overhead camshaft.
£4,000–5,000 *S*

This machine features the only known complete surviving engine of its type, produced in 1957, and exhibited at the Milan show. A set of empty cases are also known to exist but contain no mechanical internals. The engine features an indirect injection system patented by Schindele with the fuel being force-fed from a crankcase mounted rotary pump to the spray bar/mixing chamber, mounted in the conventional position for the carburettor.

c1958 MV Agusta CSS Racer 172cc.
£6,500–7,000 *AtMC*

1961 MV Agusta 150 Gran Turismo 161 149cc, single overhead valve, bore and stroke 59.5 x 54mm, 4-speed gearbox.
Est. £1,500–1,800 *S*

1966 MV Agusta 250 247cc, twin cylinder overhead valve, bore and stroke 53 x 56mm, 18bhp at 7500rpm, 5-speed gearbox.
£2,000–2,500 *S*

1970 MV Agusta RSS (Rapido Super Sport) 149cc, 5-speed gearbox, sports styling, clip-on handlebars, lightweight mudguards and humped seat.
£2,000–2,500 *S*

1971 MV Agusta 125 GTLS Sport 123.5cc, overhead valve, 5-speed gearbox, 15bhp at 8500rpm, alloy wheel rims.
£1,300–1,500 *BKS*

1972 MV Agusta 750S 743cc, 4 cylinders, double overhead camshaft.
Est. £16,000–18,000 *C*

This machine is fitted with factory optional fairing and original red, white and blue livery.

1973 MV Agusta 350B Electronica 349cc.
£1,750–2,000 *BKS*

Considered by many as the best of MV's twin cylinder models. The round case engine was much smoother than the later square case 350 Sport.

1969 MV Agusta 600 Four 591.8cc, double overhead camshaft.
Est. £10,000–11,500 *BKS*

This example has had its original twin mechanically operated Campagrolo disc brake replaced by a 4LS Grimeca drum.

Count Agusta's original 4 cylinder roadster was briefly displayed at the 1950 Milan show. Fifteen years later, at Milan in 1965, a revised version made its bow, with a 600, instead of a 500 engine. Styling was most certainly turismo rather than sport.

1970 MV Agusta 150 Sport 149cc, excellent cosmetic order.
£1,300–1,500 *BKS*

1971 MV Agusta GTLS Sport 123cc, overhead valve single cylinder, 5-speed gearbox, modified to a café racer.
Est. £1,100–1,200 *BKS*

1972 MV Agusta 350B 349cc, overhead valve twin, 5-speed gearbox, 32bhp at 7650rpm.
Est. £1,000–1,200 *BKS*

1973 MV Agusta 750S 743cc,
4 cylinders, double overhead camshaft,
4 cylinder shaft final drive, 5-speed
gearbox, 65bhp at 8500rpm, 18in
(46cm) wire wheels with Grimeca
drum brakes.
Est. £18,000–22,000 *S*

**1973 MV Agusta 350B
Electronica 349cc.
£2,700–3,000** *S*

*By increasing the bore of the 250
twin by 10mm, MV created the 350
round case model. It was
ultimately produced in a number of
guises including street scrambler,
tourer and sports model.*

**1974 MV Agusta 350B Electronica 349cc.
Est. £1,250–1,350** *BKS*

Final year of round case 350 production.

**1974 MV Agusta 350S 216
Ipotesi 349cc.
£1,200–1,400** *BKS*

1975 MV Agusta 350 Sport Ipotisi 216 349cc,
overhead valve twin cylinder square case.
£1,800–2,400 *IVC*

1975 MV Agusta 125 Sport 218 123.5cc,
overhead valve.
£1,800–2,000 *S*

*This machine is the last of many 125 class
MVs manufactured until 1977–78.*

1975 MV Agusta 125 Sport 218 123.5cc,
5-speed gearbox, 14bhp at 8500rpm, bore
and stroke 53 x 56mm, disc front brake.
£700–800 *BKS*

1977 MV Agusta 350 Sport 349cc,
overhead valve twin, 5-speed gearbox.
£3,800–4,000 *BKS*

1977 MV Agusta 350 Sport 216 Ipotesi 349cc,
square case, styled by Giorgio Gingiaro, overhead
valve twin, triple disc brakes, alloy wheels, with
optional fairing, excellent condition.
Est. £2,500–3,500 *S*

1977 MV Agusta 750 America 747cc, totally
original except for Magni curved silencers.
£12,000–13,000 *PC*

MZ *(German 1953–)*

1976 MZ TS 250 Model Sports 243cc, single
cylinder 2-stroke, unrestored condition.
£150–250 *BKS*

*MZ were the successors to the original DKW factory
in Zschopau in Sachsen in what was Eastern
Germany's Democratic Republic prior to
reunification, and were their largest producers.*

NER-A-CAR
(American/British 1921–26)

Designed by American Carl A. Neracher and built
initially in the USA, the hub centre-steered Ner-A-Car
was manufactured under license in the UK by the
Sheffield Simplex Company. Production commenced
in 1922 in what had been the ABC factory in Canbury
Park Road, Kingston-upon-Thames. UK-built
Ner-A-Cars used a Sheffield Simplex 285cc 2-stroke
engine while retaining the friction drive transmission of
the US original. Later versions were built with side and
overhead valve 350 Blackburne engines and
3-speed gearboxes, though the basic 2-stroke friction
drive model remained on sale until production ceased
in 1926. Because of its low centre of gravity and hub
centre steering it was claimed impossible for a
Ner-A-Car to skid.

1925 Ner-A-Car 285cc, restored in
1976, with restoration record file,
old style log book and Swansea V5.
£2,750–3,000 *BKS*

*This machine was once part of the
Gangbridge Collection.*

NEW HUDSON
(British 1909–57)

The Birmingham-based New Hudson factory
started life making bicycles and added
motorcycles to the range in 1909. Motorcycle
production ceased in 1933. They continued
in business until sold to Jack Sangster, who
owned Ariel and Triumph, in 1939, and with
the outbreak of war were sold again and
manufacture ceased.

The name was revived by BSA after 1945,
when they produced mopeds with 98cc Villiers
engines, in contrast to the big V-twins also
made by New Hudson in pre-WWI days.

1913 New Hudson 2¼hp, restored
but original apart from the saddle.
£1,400–1,600 *BKS*

l. **1915 New Hudson Model C Tourist 2¼hp 211cc,** single
cylinder 2-stroke, New Hudson 2-speed countershaft gearbox.
£700–900 *BKS*

*New Hudson's 2-stroke lightweight range of motorcycles were
built around the time of WWI and catered for the new
motorcyclist. 'Upwards of 100 miles per gallon' was claimed and
the bike sold for £33 when new.*

1921 New Hudson 150cc, single cylinder,
2-speed gearbox, in running order.
£2,000–2,200 *BKS*

1926 New Hudson HT3 De Luxe 597cc, side valve,
Sturmey Archer 3-speed gearbox, fully restored.
Est. £7,750–8,000 *BKS*

*The prefix 'H' is for Heavyweight, the 'T' for Tourist
and the '3' for electric lighting.*

l. **1955 New Hudson Autocycle 98cc,** Villiers
2-stroke engine, new brakes.
£250–350 *PS*

*A popular utility machine of late pre-war and early
post-war era. After 1945 the model was manufactured
by the BSA Group.*

NEW IMPERIAL
(British 1910–39)

**1937 New Imperial Model 76 De Luxe Twin Port
Sports 496cc,** overhead valve unit construction.
£3,500–4,000 *BLM*

1937 New Imperial Model 90 245cc, overhead
valve, rigid frame, girder forks, hand-operated
gear change.
£1,200–1,750 *PM*

NIMBUS *(Danish 1920–57)*

1937 New Imperial Model 76 De Luxe 499cc,
overhead valve, fully restored to concours standard.
£3,200–3,400 *BKS*

c1939 Nimbus 750cc, 4 cylinders.
£5,500–6,000 *AtMC*

NORMAN
(British 1937–61)

1951 Norman B2 197cc, 2-stroke Villiers engine,
swinging arm rear suspension.
£500–1,000 *CRC*

1956 Norman 98cc.
£75–100 *CStC*

NORTON (British 1902–)
First TT Victory

An unofficial world championship, the Coupe International des Motorcyclettes was staged during 1904 and 1905 in the French town of Dourden. Not wishing to be left out in the cold the British Auto Cycle Club (the forerunner of the ACU) decided at their 1906 dinner in London to run a motorcycle Tourist Trophy. The idea came from H. W. Staner, the then editor of *The Motor Cycle*. He asked why there could not be an event with limits on engine capacity and machine weight, with the object of demonstrating the reliability and efficiency of roadster mounts.

The ACC committee took up the idea, but decided a better way of exploiting the touring aspect would be to put emphasis on fuel consumption. The Isle of Man was chosen because of the 20mph speed limit in other parts of the UK. The Isle of Man, with its own parliament, could not only close its roads but its authorities were by then accustomed to collaborating in the organisation of speed events and welcomed 'racers' with open arms.

To select a suitable course a party from the mainland visited the Isle of Man early in 1907; they chose a triangular 15 miles, 1,430yd circuit which started and finished in St John's by the Tynwald Hill.

On the morning of Tuesday 28th May 1907, 17 singles and 8 twins paraded at St John's to have their petrol measured out. The singles were allowed one gallon for every 90 miles, the twins, one for every 75.

The quickest rider was Rembrandt Fowler on a Norton, who put in a fastest lap of 42.91mph whilst taking victory in the twin cylinder class (the singles category was won by Matchless mounted Charlie Collier). Fowler's Norton featured a French Peugeot V-twin engine of 726cc. The inlet valves worked automatically, the exhaust valves were controlled by pushrods. There was no gearbox, and the rear wheel was directly driven by a belt. Maximum speed was 62mph.

Although Fowler won only once, he was one of the best-known personalities of the TT, attending every event until his death in 1966 at the age of 85.

The Peugeot V-twin engine was soon abandoned by Norton, who thereafter developed a series of their own single cylinder engines culminating with the famous double overhead camshaft Manx.

1932 Norton Model 40 International 348cc.
£4,000–4,500 *BKS*

This machine has been used previously for competition and is in modified trim. It would be possible to either restore it to road use or continue using it in some form of competition. It is known that it was raced by Ron Langston at Mallory Park in the early 1970s in vintage races and has not been used since.

1933 Norton Manx International 350cc,
excellent original works bike, original condition.
£11,000–12,000 *SW*

1935 Norton Model 30 International 490cc,
excellent order, frame appears modified for racing, not road registered.
£4,200–4,500 *BKS*

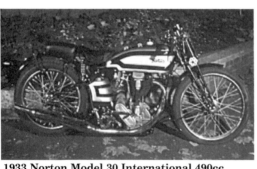

1933 Norton Model 30 International 490cc,
original log book and Swansea V5.
£4,200–4,500 *BKS*

r. **1935 Norton Model 30 International 490cc,**
excellent order, frame appears modified for racing, not road registered.
£4,200–4,500 *BKS*

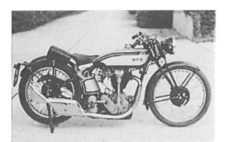

1936 Norton International 490cc.
£4,800–5,200 *BKS*

1937 Norton International/Manx 499cc Special,
1936 Electron 500cc racing unit, fitted with rev
counter, Andre steering damper, 4-speed gearbox.
£4,800–5,200 *BKS*

*Originally built as a 350cc International, the
machine was subsequently fitted with a Manx 500cc
engine specially prepared for hill climbs and
vintage racing.*

1937 Norton 16H 500cc, ex-Army.
£1,800–2,000 *PM*

1939 Norton Model 30 International 499cc,
engine in excellent condition, cycle parts and
paint are all good, Brooklands 'can' exhaust,
telescopic forks and full lighting equipment.
Est. £4,500–5,500 *S*

*This is a good example of Norton's sporting
overhead camshaft single.*

1938 Norton Model 30 International 490cc,
overhead camshaft.
£4,500–5,000 *BKS*

*In 1938 the International model had an option
priced at around £15 for the choice of rear
suspension, as used by the works riders in the
previous 2 seasons racing.*

1940 Norton 16H 490cc, side valve, ex-Army.
£1,300–1,500 *AT*

1946 Norton Manx 30M 499cc, alloy cylinder head and
barrel, large Amal carburettor, megaphone exhaust, close
ratio gearbox, plunger rear suspension, roadholder telescopic
forks, 8in (20cm) front brake with air-scoop, racing tyres,
short mudguards, large petrol tank, one gallon oil tank, both
with quick action caps, racing plates, saddle and rear pad,
tachometer, flyscreen and chin-pad, very good condition,
original log book.
Est. £10,500–12,000 *COYS*

*If there is one machine that epitomises Britain's once
indisputable standing as a leader in international motorcycle
racing it is the Norton Manx. A familiar and formidable force
on the track, it was ultimately to remain at the forefront of
competition for well over a decade.*

1947 Norton Manx 30M 499cc.
£8,300–8,700 *BKS*

During 1946 Norton built a few road racing machines. These were supplied in time for the Manx Grand Prix, and were the first to carry the simple Manx Norton name. They were listed as the 348cc Model 40M and the 499cc Model 30M. Both had single overhead camshaft engines with shaft and bevel drive to the cambox, conical hubs, a massive fuel tank and an oil tank which held a full imperial gallon of lubricant. Known as 'Garden Gate' Manx.

1947 Norton International 30 490cc,
overhead camshaft.
£15,000–16,000 *BKS*

Lancashire comedian George Formby OBE, who died in 1961, is still a legend. During a career spanning 40 years, he made 22 box office hit films, cut hundreds of records and progressed successfully from music hall to theatre, from theatre to screen and from screen to television. From 1938 to 1944 he was Britain's biggest star at the box office. Among the films he made was No Limit, a spoof on the 1935 TT races, shown for years after his death during TT week on the Isle of Man, and one of his most successful songs – sung to the accompaniment of his ukelele – was Riding in the TT Races.

George was, in fact, an enthusiastic biker, and between 1946 and 1951 alone he owned examples of Scott, Matchless G3LC, James Captain, Royal Enfield Model G and Vincent Rapide Series C, all supplied by Kings of Oxford's Manchester branch. After George and his wife Beryl had been to the Norton works in Bracebridge Street to do the lunchtime radio show Workers' Playtime, he was presented by the works with the 1947 Norton International shown here, and that too had been supplied by Kings' Manchester branch.

1947 Norton ES2 490cc, overhead valve single, restored, traditional Norton silver and black livery, Swansea V5.
£1,800–2,200 *BKS*

1947 Norton Manx 40M 348cc.
£7,500–8,000 *BKS*

Locate the Source
The source of each illustration in ***Miller's Classic Motorcycles Price Guide*** **can easily be found by checking the code letters at the end of each caption with the Key to Illustrations on Page 5.**

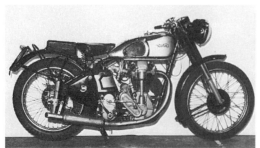

1948 Norton International 40 348cc, single cylinder overhead camshaft, in running order, fair condition.
£4,000–4,250 *PS*

Immediate post-war version of the famous International overhead camshaft model. Sprung front and rear. A similar machine was used by Geoff Duke to win the Manx Grand Prix that year.

1948 Norton ES2 490cc.
£2,000–2,500 *PM*

1949 Norton 500T Trials 490cc, overhead valve, all alloy engine, good condition.
Est. £3,000–4,000 *S*

1951 Norton 500T Trials 490cc, overhead valve single, restored to original condition, full documented history.
£4,000–4,200 *PVE*

r. 1954 Norton Twin Model 7 500cc.
£2,000–3,000 *CRC*

First of the many Norton twins. The original Model 7 appeared in 1949 with a plunger frame and new laid-down gearbox.

1948 Norton Manx Model 40 348cc, mechanically sound, 'Garden Gate' version.
Est. £7,500–7,750 *BKS*

1949 Norton ES2 490cc.
£2,800–3,000 *VER*

1950 Norton International Model 30 490cc, matching frame and engine numbers, concours condition.
£5,500–6,500 *SW*

1951 Norton International Model 30 Racing 490cc.
Est. £9,000–12,000 *BKS*

This bike was prepared by the factory for the 1951 Clubman's TT.

1954 Norton Model 19S 597cc, overhead valve.
£2,750–3,000 *MAY*

Big single for solo or sidecar use.

1957 Norton Model 19S 597cc, single cylinder.
£2,000–3,000 *CRC*

1959 Norton 99 Wideline 596cc.
£4,000–4,500 *BKS*

1959 Norton Dominator 99 596cc, Wideline frame,
short road holder forks, alloy rims, rev counter.
£2,800–3,200 *BLM*

1959 Norton Dominator 99 597cc, overhead valve,
non-standard mudguards.
£2,800–3,200 *BKS*

1955 Norton 16H 498cc.
£1,750–2,000 *BKS*

1958 Norton Model 99 597cc, twin cylinder,
Featherbed frame, alloy wheel rims.
£2,500–3,500 *CRC*

1959 Norton Jubilee 249cc, twin cylinder,
overhead valve.
£500–1,000 *CRC*

1959 Norton Jubilee 249cc.
£800–880 *BLM*

*In 1958 Norton reached its Diamond Jubilee.
To celebrate the occasion a new twin with
parallel forward sloping cylinders was
introduced. Unfortunately, although a good
looking machine, it didn't prove popular.*

1960 Norton ES2 490cc, overhead single.
£2,000–2,500 *BKS*

*This machine is a fine example of the 490cc
single cylinder ES2, one of the longest running
series designations during Norton production.
The ES2 is renowned for sheer practicality, long
hard use and faithful service to its owner.*

1961 Norton Manx 30M 499cc, non-standard
Beart-type tank, CRMC approved track silencer.
£15,000–16,000 *PC*

1961 Norton Navigator Twin 350cc.
£800–1,000 *AT*

1961 Norton Dominator 99 596cc.
£2,750–3,000 *BKS*

1962 Norton 650 646cc, overhead valve twin,
excellent handling, brakes and performance.
£2,300–2,500 *BLM*

1962 Norton Navigator de Luxe 349cc.
Est. £700–1,000 *S*

*Larger version of the 250cc Jubilee. The Navigator
was produced from 1960–65.*

1962 Norton Manx Model 30M Racing 499cc.
£14,750–15,500 *BKS*

*Although most of this machine, including the
engine, dates from 1962, an earlier single-sided
front brake is fitted.*

1962 Norton Model 50 350cc, original
condition, untouched.
£2,400–2,600 *BLM*

*Classic heavyweight British overhead valve
single with the benefits of Featherbed frame,
roadholder forks and full width brakes.*

1966 Norton Big Four Solo 597cc,
partly restored, unregistered.
Est. £1,200–1,400 *HOLL*

1968 Norton Mercury 650cc.
£2,000–2,250 *AT*

A most useable late Featherbed.

1972 Norton Commando Roadster 745cc,
Lockhead disc, upswept silencers, small tank.
£2,500–3,000 *BLM*

1972 Norton Commando 750cc, very good overall condition, original café racer parts fitted.
£1,500–2,000 *SW*

1975 Norton Commando MkIII Interstate 829cc.
£2,800–3,200 *BKS*

1988 Norton Rotary Commander 588cc, completely original including fairing and panniers, only 17,000 miles, good condition.
£3,500–4,000 *BKS*

This machine comes with a letter from Norton Motors confirming that it was the first civilian machine to leave the Shenstone, Lichfield factory.

1972 Norton Commando Roadster 745cc, twin cylinder, isolastic suspension.
£3,000–4,000 *CRC*

1988 Norton Classic Rotary 588cc, twin rotary, air-cooled.
£5,500–6,500 *CRC*

Only 100 of these machines were produced.

NSU
(German 1901–65)

1955 NSU Special Max 247cc, overhead camshaft, original and immaculate condition.
£2,500–2,800 *PC*

Together with BMW, NSU built high class motorcycles in the 1950s.

OK SUPREME
(British 1899–1939)

OK motorcycles were in production in the last years of the 19thC, continuing until the outbreak of hostilities in 1939. Proprietary engines were adopted in the vintage years, including Bradshaw, Blackburne and JAP. The JAP engined bikes in particular took OK to many track victories. Supreme was added to the name OK in later years.

1936 OK Supreme G37 Flying Cloud 245cc.
£1,600–1,800 *BKS*

The lightweight overhead valve 250 Model G37 was one of 10 models offered by the company for the 1937 season.

l. **1934 OK Supreme Flying Cloud 245cc,** single cylinder overhead valve, total loss oil system.
£2,000–3,000 *CRC*

PANTHER (P&M)
(British 1900–66)

'The Perfected Motorcycle' was a slogan first coined for the Phelon & Moore (P&M) catalogue in 1911. Even before Phelon & Moore was founded in 1904 Joah Phelon's patented sloping engine had firmly established itself in the motorcycling world being fitted to the Humber from 1901 onwards. As for Joah Phelon, he had dreamed of motorised transport since as early as 1895. In 1901 he took out a patent covering the 'use of the engine in place of the downtube – a series of long bolts to hold the main bearings, cylinder and head as one unit to contain stress'.

The Panther name was first used in the 1920s and applied to only one model, but in time the whole range, even though the company remained P&M, carried the Panther emblem. Just to confuse the issue further there was also a German Panther which existed between 1896 and 1975. There was no financial connection, in fact the only thing the two companies shared was a trademark featuring a panther's head.

Besides its famous sloping single cylinder engine format, the Cleckheaton-based P&M concern did experiment with other types of engine including 750 and 770cc prototype 90 degree V-twins, the 247cc Panthette Twin 600cc vertical cylinder single in both 500cc overhead valve and 600cc side valve (the latter for export only). The most interesting of all was a very advanced Bradshaw designed vertical in-line twin.

During WWII P&M made aircraft parts, but late in 1945 came news of their re-introduction of the Panther motorcycle range. There were three models listed, the 60, 70 and 100. All were overhead valve, with capacities of 249, 348 and 594cc respectively; all featured the classic sloping cylinder.

The use of an engine with vertical cylinder came in 1949, with the models 65 and 75 replacing the 60 and 70 slopers. Together with the 594 'Big Cat' sloper these made up the Panther range for the 1950s. To supplement the model line Villiers 2-stroke powered models in 174, 197, 249 and 324cc engine sizes were brought in, beginning with the 10/3 and 10/4 with 197cc engines in 1956. There was even a scooter, the Princess (1960) with a 174cc Villiers 2L motor.

Into the 1960s the Villiers engined models continued, together with three motorcycles with the famous Panther 'sloper', the 594cc Standard 100 and De Luxe 100, and the larger 645cc 120. The extra capacity came from just one extra millimetre on the bore and six more on the stroke, giving 88 x 106mm dimensions.

The final year of manufacture came in 1966, with just two models remaining. They were the 249cc 35 2-stroke twin and the 120 645 overhead valve single.

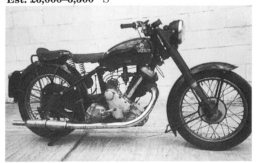

1920 Panther 3½hp 499cc, excellent refurbished condition.
Est. £6,000–6,500 S

1954 Panther MD100 594cc, original condition.
£2,000–2,200 AT

r. **1956 Panther 10/3 197cc,** 2-stroke Villiers engine, leading link front fork, original condition.
£300–500 CRC

1922 Panther 2¾hp, requires restoration.
£2,000–2,500 S

1956 Panther Model 100 594cc, overhead valve, big twin port sloper single, swinging arm rear suspension, full width hubs, telescopic front forks.
£1,000–1,500 MAY

PARILLA
(Italian 1946–67)

1965 Parilla Fox Racer 174cc.
£2,500–3,000 *BKS*

The high-cam Fox racer is typical of Parilla designs, – clean and functional. The factory built bikes between 1946 and 1967 before financial troubles forced them to switch to producing to kart engines.

PREMIER
(British 1908–15)

1914 Premier 3½hp, 3-speed gearbox, restored.
£5,800–6,500 *BKS*

Premier of Coventry built motorcycles from 1908 to 1915, initially V-twin machines, and in later years mainly sturdy singles.

RALEIGH
(British 1899–1970s)

A household name in pedal cycles, Raleigh of Nottingham also made motorcycles from 1899 to 1906 and then again from 1919 until the early '30s. The firm also controlled the Sturmey-Archer gearbox and engine factory, and supplied many other British and Continental manufacturers.

1922 Raleigh 2¾hp 350cc, inlet over exhaust engine, caliper brakes, inverted control levers, footboards and forward mounted magneto.
£2,000–2,500 *HOLL*

POPE
(American 1911–18)

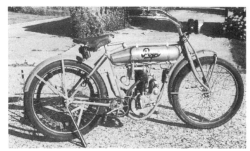

1912 Pope 500cc.
£7,500–8,000 *AtMC*

PUCH
(Austrian 1891–1990)

1959 Puch 246cc, 2-stroke, split single.
£700–800 *CRC*

1978 Puch Monza 49cc, 2-stroke, 4-speed gearbox.
£480–550 *BKS*

1930 Raleigh Sprint 500cc, overhead valve.
£1,800–2,200 *BKS*

RAVAT
(French 1898–late 1950s)

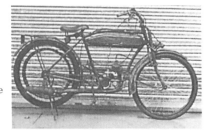

r. **1924 Ravat Type ER 98cc,** 2-stroke air-cooled engine, Longuemare carburettor and magneto ignition, belt final drive with pedal assitance, sprung front forks, beaded edge wheels rebuilt, new tyres and tubes fitted in 1981, stored since, restoration project.
£400–500 *BKS*

ROYAL ENFIELD
(British 1901–70)

1915 Royal Enfield 300cc, V-twin, overhead valve, variable speed, foot boards, chain drive, kick start, glass oil reservoirs.
£5,500–6,000 *BLM*

1925 Royal Enfield Sports 2¾hp.
£2,000–2,500 *BLM*

1928 Royal Enfield 350cc, overhead valve single, 3-speed hand change gearbox, girder forks, rigid rear frame, luggage carrier and horn, magneto requires attention, stored since the late 1970s, with V5.
£1,850–2,000 *BKS*

1939 Royal Enfield CM 346cc, magdyno overhead valve, Albion 4-speed gearbox, girder forks, original and complete, with Swansea V5.
£1,500–1,800 *BKS*

1951 Royal Enfield Bullet G 346cc.
£1,500–1,800 *BLM*

1921 Royal Enfield Lightweight 225cc, all major parts present but incomplete, a rewarding restoration project.
£350–500 *BKS*

1927 Royal Enfield 348cc, side valve single, 3-speed hand change gearbox, girder forks, engine and gearbox overhauled, magneto not working, with V5.
£2,000–2,500 *BKS*

1933 Royal Enfield Model B 248cc, single cylinder side valve, 4-speed hand change gearbox, dry sump lubrication, in original condition, optional leg shields, with original tool kit and Swansea V5.
£1,200–1,400 *BKS*
This machine sold for £39 new.

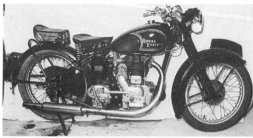

1951 Royal Enfield G2 346cc, single overhead valve.
£1,000–1,500 *CRC*

1951 Royal Enfield Bullet Trials 346cc, completely renovated and modified to pre-1965 Trial trim 3 years ago, with current V5.
£1,000–1,200 *BKS*

The Royal Enfield factory introduced its new prototype 346cc Bullet by entering their 1948 Works Team using the new model. The team won gold medals and the trophy outright.

1952 Royal Enfield Model J2 499cc, original
unrestored condition.
Est. £700–800 *MR*

1953 Royal Enfield 499cc, single, good, original
condition but needs recommissioning, with
Swansea V5.
£1,500–1,800 *BKS*

**1954 Royal Enfield G2 Bullet Ex-Works
Trials 346cc,** low ratio trials gearbox,
TT magneto, with V5.
Est. £3,000–3,500 *S*

*This machine was part of the Stanley Robinson
Collection from 1982 to 1993. During this time it
underwent a major mechanical overhaul.*

c1957 Royal Enfield Bullet Trials 346cc,
substantially rebuilt including new shocks, wheels,
tyres, carburettor and alloy mudguards.
£1,750–2,000 *BKS*

*This is the ex-Ken Carrington machine and since
its rebuild is ready to use and win on.*

1959 Royal Enfield Meteor Minor 496cc,
twin cylinder, original, unrestored condition,
with Swansea V5.
£850–1,000 *S*

Formerly part of the Anthony Durose collection.

1959 Royal Enfield Constellation 692cc,
overhead valve twin.
Est. £2,800–3,000 *BKS*

*At the end of the 1950s Royal Enfield machines were
being marketed in America under the Indian name.
As a result the Enfield machines gained a high
reputation in the endurance cross country type events
of which the Americans were exponents. In 500cc
events the single cylinder models built their
reputation high scoring win after win in flat-track
racing. This brought a demand for a high capacity
road burner twin and, as a result, the 692cc
Constellation was created.*

1959 Royal Enfield Constellation 696cc,
concours condition.
£3,000–3,250 *PC*

1959 Royal Enfield Bighead Bullet 499cc, overhead valve single
cylinder engine, Albion posi-stop gearbox, magneto ignition and
angled sidelights, good condition throughout, with Swansea V5.
£2,500–3,000 *BKS*

One of only 7 built in 1959.

1960 Royal Enfield 150 Prince 148cc,
trials conversion, good mechanical order.
£370–450 *BKS*

1961 Royal Enfield Clipper 248cc,
good condition.
£900–1,100 *BLM*

1961 Royal Enfield Crusader Sports 248cc,
overhead valve, Gold Star pattern silencer,
otherwise original.
£1,000–2,000 *CRC*

**1961 Royal Enfield Constellation
692cc,** overhead twin.
£2,000–3,000 *CRC*

**1962 Royal Enfield Continental GT Racer
248cc,** 5-speed gearbox, recently rebuilt.
Est. £1,100–1,300 *BKS*

1962 Royal Enfield Bullet 348cc.
£1,000–1,400 *CStC*

1963 Royal Enfield Continental 248cc,
some parts missing including exhaust.
£300–350 *PS*

1964 Royal Enfield Crusader Sports 248cc.
£600–700 *PS*

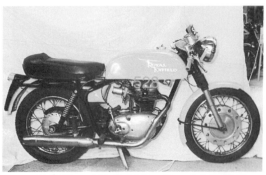

1965 Royal Enfield Continental GT 248cc,
5-speed gearbox, single cylinder café racer.
£1,000–1,750 *CRC*

1965 Royal Enfield Interceptor 736cc.
£3,000–4,000 *REOC*

1965 Royal Enfield Continental 248cc, only 29,000 miles recorded, good running order, original farings, correct side panels, Swansea V5.
Est. £700–800 *BKS*

1967 Royal Enfield Continental GT 248cc, excellent condition.
£2,000–2,500 *PVE*

1967 Royal Enfield Continental GT 248cc, overhead valve, 4-speed gearbox, new tyres, chain and shock absorbers, good mechanical condition.
Est. £1,500–1,800 *BKS*

ROVER *(British 1902–25)*

1911 Rover 5hp Single Speed, very good original condition, with Swansea V5.
£5,700–6,500 *BKS*

Rover, although now best known for their cars, made motorcycles of sound design and excellent workmanship from 1902 until 1925.

1920 Rover 4½hp, single cylinder side valve, Ariel gearbox with silent tooth drive, rear drum brake, spring link drive, with luggage grid and leather toolboxes, Swansea V5, good condition throughout.
£3,000–4,000 *BKS*

c1930 Rover 250cc, unit construction, very rare.
£3,000–4,000 *AtMC*

RUDGE *(British 1911–40)*

1912 Rudge TT 499cc, single speed belt drive, rigid rear frame, oil syringe mounted in the tank, with luggage grid and leather toolbox.
£5,000–6,000 *BKS*

Rudge-Whitworth machines were made until 1940, and it has been said that the closure of the factory was one of the greatest losses the British motorcycle industry ever experienced.

c1910 Rudge Single 499cc.
£7,000–8,000 *AtMC*

1926 Rudge-Whitworth 499cc, overhead valve with 4 valves per cylinder, 4-speed gearbox, coupled brakes, period lighting set, luggage carrier, very good condition throughout, Swansea V5.
£3,000–3,400 *BKS*

1928 Rudge TT Special 499cc, webbed crankcase, large drum brakes, very good overall condition, Swansea V5.
£3,500–4,000 *S*

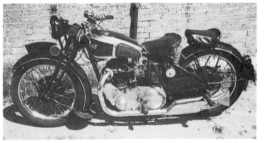

1934 Rudge Special 500cc, good original condition.
£2,800–3,250 *AT*

1937 Rudge Special 499cc, 4-valve twin port, pent roof, good original condition, Swansea V5.
£2,500–3,000 *S*

1937 Rudge Special 499cc, 4-valve single, pent roof, concours condition, Swansea V5.
£5,000–5,500 *BKS*

1939 Rudge Special 499cc, requires restoration.
£3,500–4,000 *BKS*

1939 Rudge Ulster 499cc, overhead camshaft, semi-radial 4-valve.
Est. £3,900–4,100 *BKS*

Rudge were famous for their Ulster GP wins naming their twin port single super sports model the Ulster, a name which remained until the end of the series in 1939. The famous bronze head became synonymous with the model.

SCOTT
(British 1909–late 1960s)

1921 Scott Squirrel 2 Speed Solo 498cc,
2-stroke, rotary valve, water-cooled, telescopic forks,
finished in the distinctive Scott colours of maroon
and black, good original condition.
£2,500–3,000 *C*

1929 Scott TT Replica 498cc, water-cooled, well
presented machine.
£2,800–3,200 *BKS*

1928 Scott Open Frame Super Squirrel 596cc,
2-speed gearbox, restored, excellent condition
throughout.
Est. £4,500–5,500 *C*

1929 Scott TT Replica 498cc, restored, new tyres,
radiator and exhaust, Swansea V5.
£5,600–6,500 *C*

1925/29 Scott Super Squirrel 596cc,
2-speed, big-bore cylinder block, rebuilt by
Tom Ward of Derby in 1973, museum
displayed in recent years, Swnsea V5.
£3,500–4,000 *BKS*

*This machine was once part of The
Gangbridge Collection.*

1927 Scott Two Speed Flying Squirrel 498cc,
P&H acetylene lighting, passenger pillion seat,
leather tool panniers, requires careful
recommissioning, Swansea V5.
£3,000–3,500 *BKS*

1929 Scott Flying Squirrel 498cc, twin
2-stroke engine, water-cooled, girder forks,
coil spring suspension, rigid rear frame,
good condition.
£3,000–3,500 *BKS*

1934 Scott Flying Squirrel 498cc, 3-speed
gearbox, girder forks, restored, Swansea V5.
Est. £2,500–2,800 *BKS*

*This machine was once part of The
Gangbridge Collection.*

1937 Scott 500cc, water-cooled twin.
£2,000–2,400 *AT*

SEELEY *(British 1966–70s)*

Many times British sidecar champion Colin Seeley bought Associated Motorcycles' racing department when the company went into receivership in 1966. The previous year he had constructed the first Seeley racing frame to house a Matchless G50 engine. The AMC purchase enabled him to produce complete Seeley G50 and 7R machines. With their improved frames, the ageing 4-stroke singles enjoyed renewed competitiveness, with Dave Croxford winning the British 500 Championship on a Seeley G50 in 1968 and '69. The Seeley frame progressed from the Duplex cradle MkI to the similar but lighter MkII, before the downtubes were abandoned with the MkIII, the headstock and swinging arm pivot of which were linked solely by tubes running diagonally above the engine. The MkIV introduced in 1970 featured a revised tubing layout and continued in production until 1973.

c1972 Seeley G50 MkIV 496cc.
£8,500–9,500 *BKS*

1978 Seeley Honda Superbike 810cc, Yoshimura Hemmings engine, new battery, duplex cradle frame in Reynolds chrome molybdenum tubing, fully braced swinging arm, unique precision chain adjustment developed from Seeley's racing machines, Lester wheels, 5.5 gallon fuel tank, fairing, V5.
Est. £5,000–5,500 *BKS*

Designed by Colin Seeley for road use, but to his racing standards.

SERTUM *(Italian 1931–51)*

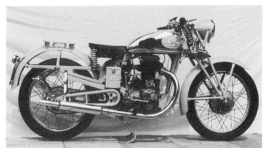

1947 Sertum 250 Sport 249cc, overhead valve, restored, rare.
£5,000–5,500 *IVC*

SPRITE
(British 1965–71)

Sprite machines were produced by Frank Hipkin and Fred Evans, mainly as a result of Frank Hipkin's success on machines of his own manufacture. They first appeared in scrambler guise in 1964 fitted with a duplex frame and AMC heavyweight forks. However, by 1965 when the trials model appeared, fitted with a Villiers 2-stroke single, an Earles type fork had become the standard fitting, although the steering head was engineered to accept AMC, BSA or Cerani forks as an alternative.

1965 Sprite Trials 247cc, engine and gearbox overhauled, cycle parts refinished to a high standard, in good running order.
Est. £900–1,500 *S*

SPARKBROOK
(British 1912–25)

1921 Sparkbrook Solo 250cc, single, 2-stroke, TT type drop handles, 2-speed gearbox, oil pump to the flat tank, belt drive, rare.
£1,800–2,000 *HOLL*

STEVENS
(British 1934–37)

1936 Stevens Sports 350cc, overhead valve, air-cooled, 3-speed gearbox, single pan saddle, Swansea V5, in need of complete restoration, rare.
£1,400–1,500 *BKS*

This machine has recently been assembled after being stored, for approximately 20 years, in packing cases.

SUNBEAM *(British 1912–57)*

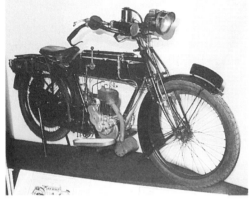

1913 Sunbeam 3½hp, side valve.
£4,000–5,000 *VMCC*

1921 Sunbeam TT Replica 500cc,
restored to very good order throughout.
Est. £3,500–3,800 *BKS*

1924 Sunbeam Sprint 498cc.
£13,000–14,500 *PM*

1927 Sunbeam 346cc, side valve, very
good original condition throughout having
been carefully dry-stored in a private
collection for the past 20 years, luggage
carrier, leather toolboxes, Swansea V5.
£3,500–4,000 *BKS*

1919 Sunbeam 3½hp, side valve.
£5,500–6,500 *VER*

1923 Sunbeam 500cc and Sidecar.
£5,000–6,000 *VER*

1924 Sunbeam Sprint Special 493cc, Binks
'mousetrap' racing carburettor, 3-speed close ratio
gearbox, Brooklands silencer, very good condition
throughout, Swansea V5.
£16,500–18,000 *BKS*

*This machine is one of the first Sprint Sunbeams, is
rare and won the George Dance Trophy at the 1995
Sunbeam Rally.*

1927 Sunbeam Long Stroke Model 6 492cc,
engine, gearbox and frame in sound condition,
magneto ignition, carburettor and leather tool
boxes recently reconditioned, acetylene lighting
system front and rear, Swansea V5.
£2,500–3,000 *BKS*

l. **1928 Sunbeam Model TT90 493cc,**
reconditioned engine, frame and forks, 3-speed
gearbox, TT exhaust pipes, short silencers, auxiliary
oil feed to the engine, excellent condition, rare,
Swansea V5.
£11,500–13,000 *BKS*

1928 Sunbeam Model 8 346cc, overhead valve, in good running order, Swansea V5.
Est. £4,200–4,500 *S*

1929 Sunbeam Model 1 346cc, side valve, original condition.
£2,500–3,000 *PC*

1930 Sunbeam Model 9 493cc, overhead valve, girder forks, rigid rear frame, pillion seat, Swansea V5, restoration project.
£3,000–3,500 *BKS*

1931 Sunbeam Model 8 346cc, overhead valve.
£3,400–3,600 *VER*

In 1928 Sunbeam became part of the ICI organisation but this was not always a happy relationship. Sunbeam won 4 Senior TTs in the 1920s, along with many other races.

1932 Sunbeam Lion 489cc, single cylinder, side valve, hand change gearbox, sound original condition, Swansea V5, needs recommissioning.
£1,800–2,500 *BKS*

1933 Sunbeam Lion 489cc, side valve.
£3,700–4,000 *BLM*

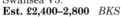

1935 Sunbeam Model 16 246cc, high camshaft, overhead valve, unrestored, Swansea V5.
Est. £2,400–2,800 *BKS*

This model was only manufactured for one year.

1935 Sunbeam 250cc, overhead valve, full electric lighting set, excellent overall condition, Swansea V5.
£2,400–2,800 *BKS*

l. **1938 Sunbeam Model 8 346cc,** good all round condition, Swansea V5.
Est. £3,600–3,800 *BKS*

Winner of the concours award in its class at the Castleford and District Motorcycle Cavalcade in 1995.

1948 Sunbeam Model S7 489cc, two-into-one exhaust system, deeply valenced mudguards, sprung riders saddle, sound condition, Swansea V5.
£2,300–2,500 *BKS*

1946 Sunbeam S7 489cc, overhead camshaft, early Sunbeam front forks, inverted control levers, restored to original condition, finished in mist green and black.
£2,500–3,000 *SOF*

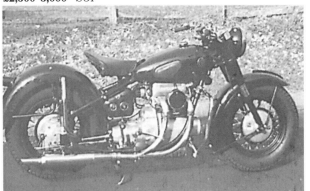

1950 Sunbeam S7 489cc, overhead camshaft, excellent example of the marque, needs mechanical and safety checks before use, Swansea V5.
£2,500–2,800 *BKS*

1950 Sunbeam 57 489cc, overhead camshaft, totally rebuilt to a high standard around 1980 when a high capacity sump, oil, temperature guages, 12 volt Lucas conversion kit with alternator and diode control and Lucas headlamp conversion, and new shaft drive were fitted, excellent rebuilt condition, Swansea V5.
£3,000–3,200 *BKS*

Stored in a de-humidified garage as part of a private collection for the past 15 years.

> **Miller's is a price GUIDE not a price LIST**

1950 Sunbeam S8 489cc, with shortened mudguards and narrow tyres, finished black and silver.
£2,000–2,500 *SOF*

r. **1951 Sunbeam S7 De Luxe 489cc,** overhead camshaft.
£2,500–3,000 *SOF*

Known as 'The Gentleman's Motorcycle'.

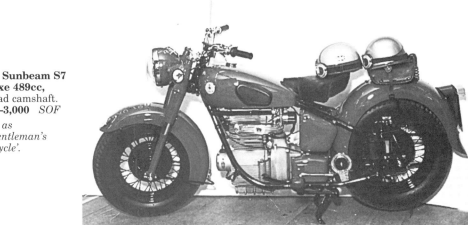

1950 Sunbeam S8 489cc, overhead
camshaft, in-line twin, coil ignition,
shaft drive.
£2,600–2,800 *BLM*

1952 Sunbeam S8 489cc, overhead camshaft, coil ignition,
concours condition, original polychromatic grey finish.
£2,600–2,800 *SOF*

1954 Sunbeam S7 489cc, shaft
drive, rubber-mounted engine.
£2,000–3,000 *CRC*

1957 Sunbeam S8 489cc, in-line twin, overhead
camshaft engine, in-unit gearbox and shaft final
drive, 23,000 miles recorded, restored to very good
condition throughout, Swansea V5.
£2,300–2,500 *BKS*

*Dry-stored in a de-humidifed building for the past
15 years as part of a private collection.*

1956 Sunbeam S8 489cc, overhead camshaft, high compression
engine, BSA forks, slim tyres, restored, Swansea V5.
£2,700–3,000 *BKS*

SUN *(British 1911–61)*

**r. 1914 Sun Villiers 269cc.
Est. £4,500–5,000** *S*

*The Sun Company, like many other motorcycle
manufacturers, started in the cycle industry but it was not
until 1911 that they produced their first motorcycle, making
use of a Villiers power-plant.*

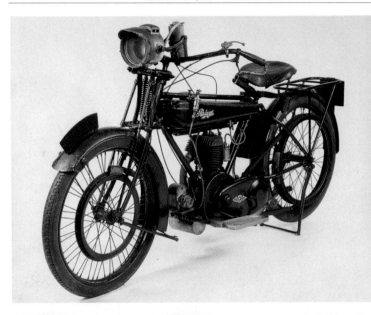

l. **1924 Raleigh 2¾hp Solo 247cc,** side valve, 3-speed gearbox, belt drive, kick start, unrestored, original condition, V5 document.
£3,400–3,800 *HOLL*

World famous for its bicycles, Raleigh built motorcycles both before and after WWI. They also sold engines and gearboxes to other makers under the Sturmey Archer name and continued until 1934. Their gearbox design was subsequently bought by Norton.

At the end of 1933, the company switched to making three-wheeler cars and vans, which it had begun 3 years earlier. This too ceased in 1935 and from then on its efforts were channelled exclusively into pedal cycles, rising to its current market leading position in post-WWII era.

1923 Raleigh 2¾hp 247cc, side valve single, good condition.
£2,600–2,800 *BLM*

This was one of the most popular Raleighs, and was manufactured until the mid-1920s.

1922 Raleigh V-Twin 800cc, good condition.
£8,000–8,500 *BLM*

Raleigh built motorcycles up to 1933.

1929 Raleigh 15 De Luxe 248cc, single cylinder, side valve, V5 document.
£2,000–2,500 *PS*

1931 Royal Enfield Model BL 225cc, single cylinder, 4-stroke, 3-speed gearbox, unsprung frame with girder forks, coil spring front suspension, good condition throughout.
£1,700–2,000 *BKS*

1930/40 Royal Enfield Model WD CO 346cc, overhead valve, good condition, ex-War Department model.
£1,500–2,000 *BLM*

1940 Royal Enfield CO 346cc, original specification, good condition.
£850–1,000 *PS*

1947 Royal Enfield CO 346cc, girder forks, rigid rear end frame, lighting set, speedometer, mudguard mounted pillion seat, good condition. **Est. £1,800–2,000** *BKS*

1951 Royal Enfield Bullet G 346cc, original S1 model, unused for 2 years, V5 document, good condition. **£1,400–1,800** *PS*

1952 Royal Enfield G2 Bullet 346cc, overhead valve single, excellent condition. **£3,000–3,500** *REOC*

1959 Royal Enfield Constellation 696cc, twin cylinder, magneto ignition, only 7,600 miles, V5 document, original condition. **Est. £2,600–2,800** *BKS*

1959 Royal Enfield Indian Chief 693cc, very good condition. **£12,000–13,000** *REOC*

Only 55 were manufactured, 50 of which were for the New York Police Department.

1970 Royal Enfield Indian Clymer 736cc, very good condition. **£7,200–7,500** *REOC*

Manufactured in Bologna, Italy, very few were made.

1966 Royal Enfield Continental 248cc, 5-speed gearbox, factory café racer, concours condition. **£2,300–2,500** *REOC*

1961 Royal Enfield Crusader Sports 248cc, 4-speed gearbox, 70 x 64.5mm, good condition. **£1,000–1,300** *BLM*

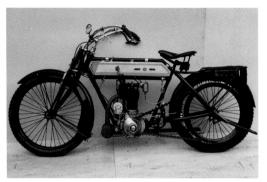

1911 Rudge 500cc, very good condition.
£5,500–6,500 *VER*

1921 Rudge Multi Speed 500cc,
belt drive, original condition.
£2,000–3,000 *PC*

1928 Rudge TT 348cc Replica, twin port,
4-valve single.
Est. £3,300–3,600 *BKS*

1936/7 Rudge 493cc Special, single
cylinder, overhead valve, no lights,
some non-original parts, V5 document.
£1,700–2,000 *PS*

1930 Rudge TT 348cc Racer, 4-speed gearbox,
bronze cylinder head, 4 valves, totally restored,
excellent condition.
£8,000–8,500 *BKS*

1912 Rudge Multi 3½hp 499cc,
good condition.
£6,500–7,500 *VER*

1929 Rudge TT Replica 499cc, works bike No. 24,
good condition.
£12,000–14,000 *REC*

*During the 1920s and '30s Rudge established a fine
reputation as TT winners and Brooklands record holders.*

1934 Rudge TT Replica 248cc, overhead
valve, radial head, bore and stroke
62.5 x 81mm, very good condition.
£4,500–5,000 *REC*

1924 Scott 498cc, very good condition.
£3,500–4,000 *VER*

1929 Scott Flying Squirrel 596cc, water-cooled, sloping cylinders, very good condition.
£3,800–4,500 *VER*

1929 Scott Closed Frame 498cc, 2-speed gearbox, parallel twin cylinder engine, very good condition.
£5,500–6,500 *VER*

Both cranks had overhead connecting rod and flywheel located between the cylinders.

1934 Scott Flying Squirrel 498cc, 2-stroke, girder forks, rigid frame at the rear, good mechanical condition.
£3,600–4,200 *BKS*

1929 Scott TT Replica 498cc, 2-stroke, twin cylinders, very good condition.
£3,500–4,500 *VER*

1970 Seeley G50 498cc, single cylinder, engine rebuilt, very good condition.
Est. £9,000–11,000 *COYS*

1972 Seeley-BSA Gold Star 499cc, special short stroke engine, Seeley chassis, very good condition.
£7,000–8,000 *CRMC*

1914 Sparkbrook 2½hp, 2-stroke, very good condition.
£2,400–2,600 *PVE*

The Sparkbrook Company was founded in 1883, and motorcycle production began shortly after the turn of the century.

1908 Triumph 3½hp, very good condition.
£5,000–5,500 *AtMC*

For a company as British as Triumph, it is interesting that this machine originated in the mind of a young German, Siegfried Bettman.

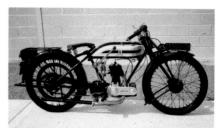

1926 Triumph Model P 500cc, very good condition.
£3,000–3,500 *BLM*

This machine cost just £42.17.6 when new.

1940s Triumph 3H 343cc, girder fork, rigid frame, ex-War Department.
£1,500–1,850 *BLM*

1924 Triumph Model SD 550cc, side valve, hand gearchange, original condition.
£2,000–3,000 *CRC*

1930 Triumph CTT 498cc, twin overhead valve single.
£4,000–5,000 *VER*

1946 Triumph 3T 349cc, rigid rear end, panel tank, pre-nacelle headlamp.
£3,350–3,850 *BLM*

1947 Triumph Speed Twin 499cc, overhead valve, sprung hub.
£3,500–4,250 *VER*

1955 Triumph Speed Twin 499cc, fully restored, period panniers, swinging arm rear suspension.
£4,000–4,500 *PC*

1957 Triumph Twenty-One 349cc, concours condition.
£3,500–4,000 *TOC*

1958 Triumph 6T Thunderbird 650cc,
pre-unit, iron cylinder and head, original
specification, only 2,000 miles since overhaul,
good condition.
£1,800–2,200 *BKS*

1960 Triumph Twenty-One 349cc, good condition.
£1,300–1,500 *MAY*

*Introduced in 1957, the Model Twenty-One or 3TA
was the first of Triumph's unit construction twins.*

1959 Trumph 3TA Twenty-One 349cc,
overhead twin, unit construction, fully restored,
non-standard bar-end mirror.
£2,500–3,000 *BLM*

Sometimes called the 'bath tub' model.

1962 Triumph Thunderbird 649cc, last pre-unit
Duplex framed with 'bath tub' rear enclosure.
£3,000–4,000 *CRC*

1975 Triumph Legend 740cc, good condition.
£7,500–8,000 *GLC*

1967 Triumph T20 S/C Super Cub 199cc,
good condition.
£800–1,000 *MAY*

*Commonly known as the Bantam Cub, this was
the last of the famous Cub series. In its final form
it sported full-width hubs and Bantam tank.*

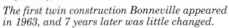

1970 Triumph T120 Bonneville 649cc,
very good condition.
£3,800–4,000 *GLC*

*The first twin construction Bonneville appeared
in 1963, and 7 years later was little changed.*

1970 Triumph T100C 490cc, overhead valve,
good condition throughout, original specification,
V5 document.
£2,000–2,200 *BKS*

This is an American model with high-level exhaust.

1927 Velocette KSS MkI 348cc, good condition.
£2,000–2,300 *PS*

*Constructed for vintage racing, this machine has
been fitted with high compression piston to run on
methanol fuel.*

1935 Velocette GTP 249cc, 2-stroke single,
twin port, twin exhaust system.
£2,000–2,500 *Vel*

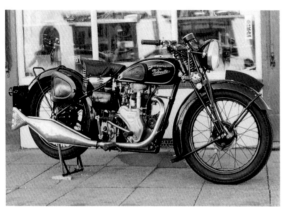

1937 Velocette MAC 349cc, overhead valve,
bore and stroke 68 x 96mm, very good condition.
£3,500–4,000 *AtMC*

*First introduced for the 1934 model year and was
to become one of Velocette's most popular models.*

1955 Velocette MSS 499cc, overhead
valve single, touring model.
£2,500–2,700 *BLM*

1938 Velocette KSS 348cc, single overhead
camshaft, good condition.
£5,000–5,500 *VER*

This model rivals Norton's famous International.

1953 Velocette LE 192cc, side valve,
flat twin, water-cooled, fully enclosed panels.
£750–800 *BKS*

Often used by police forces for patrol work.

1958 Velocette Venom 499cc, overhead valve,
very good condition.
£3,000–4,000 *Vel*

l. **1959 Velocette Venom 499cc Racer,**
very good condition.
£3,500–3,800 *PC*

*Raced in production type races during the
1950s and '60s, similar models were often
class winners in the Thruxton 500 mile race.*

1939 Vincent-HRD Series A Rapide 998cc,
overhead valve, V-twin, bore and stroke
84 x 90mm, 4-speed gearbox, good condition.
£22,000–24,000 *PM*

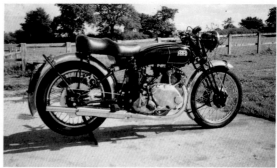

1947 Vincent-HRD Series A Meteor 499cc, good condition.
£5,500–6,000 *BLM*

The Meteor was the standard model, the Comet the sportster.

1951 Vincent Black Shadow Series C 998cc,
overhead valve, V-twin, 5in speedometer,
completely rebuilt, concours standard.
£13,500–15,000 *BKS*

*In its day, this was the fastest production
roadster in the world.*

1952 Vincent Series C Rapide 998cc,
overhead valve, V-twin, bore and stroke
84 x 90mm, good condition.
£11,000–12,000 *CRC*

1951 Vincent Black Shadow Series C 998cc,
overhead valve, V-twin, high cam, 4-stroke, bore and
stroke 84 x 90mm, 55bhp, excellent condition.
£15,000–16,000 *VER*

1952 Vincent-HRD Rapide 998cc, overhead
valve, V-twin, original specification.
£11,000–12,000 *PC*

1956 Vincent Black Knight 998cc, good condition.
£11,000–13,000 *VER*

*Built 1955, registered 1956, basically the Rapide
with slight alterations. Very few were built before
production of all Vincent motorcycles ceased.*

1952 Vincent Series C Rapide 998cc.
£11,000–13,000 *S*

*The Series C lacked the Girdraulic forks,
and resulted in only 200 machines being
produced in the first year of production.*

1920 Wanderer 415cc, V-twin, countershaft gearbox, Sturmey-Archer type gearchange lever, chain primary and final drive, fully restored, very good condition.
£3,000–4,000 *BKS*

1939 Wilkinson V4 599cc, double overhead camshaft, good condition, extremely rare.
£6,000–8,000 *VMCC*

1922 Wolf Model C 2¾hp, JAP engine, lightweight, flat tank, belt final drive.
£2,500–3,000 *BLM*

1973 Yamaha YDS7 247cc, air-cooled twin cylinder engine, 6-speed gearbox, drum brakes.
£275–325 *PS*

1978 Yamaha SR500 499cc, overhead camshaft, single cylinder, new alternator, CDI unit, up-rated rear suspension units, original condition, V5 document.
£425–500 *PS*

1978 Yamaha RD400 398cc, twin cylinder, 2-stroke, good condition.
£1,000–2,000 *CRC*

1980s Yamaha FZR 750 749cc, mechanically sound, excellent condition.
£2,500–3,000 *BKS*

As raced by Locktite Yamaha racing team in the late 1980s.

1985 Yamaha XVZ 1200cc, fairing, panniers and top box standard equipment.
£3,500–4,000 *MWM*

This was the touring model to challenge Honda's Gold Wing, but was never officially imported into the UK.

1974 Benelli 250 2C 231.4cc Racer, alloy tank, expansion chambers, tuned engine, close box.
£2,300–2,500 *PC*

A one-off machine built by Australian Norm Westerman.

1976 Ducati 900SS, good condition, V5 document.
£6,750–7,000 *BKS*

This machine was ridden by Dave Cartwright to many victories between 1977 and 1980.

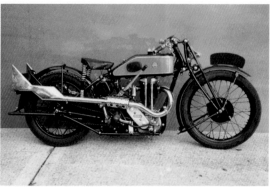

1927 Triumph 500cc TT Racer, very good condition.
£8,000–9,000 *VER*

This machine was built in pre-Jack Sangster days.

1953 Matchless G45 498cc Racer, good condition.
£16,000–18,000 *VER*

The early production of G45 of 1953–55 differed from the original factory prototype in respect of tanks, gearchange and rev counter drive.

1972 Seeley G50 496cc Racer, good condition.
£10,000–11,000 *CRMC*
Sidecar racer, Colin Seeley, purchased stock and rights to manufacture AJS 7R & Matchless G50 racers.

1969/73 Triumph Daytona 490cc Solo Racer, Carillo rods, balanced crank, large valve head, close ratio gearbox, excellent condition.
Est. £3,500–4,500 *S*

l. **1954 MV Agusta 500/4 497.5cc Works Racer,** double overhead camshaft, 4 cylinders, 5-speeds, air-cooled, chain drive, later telescopic forks, double-sided front brake, overhauled, good condition.
Est. £75,000–100,000 *S*

Five machines were built for the 1954 season, of which this is one, and it was probably raced throughout that season and the subsequent 2 seasons.

c1968 Weslake Triton 750cc Café Racer, overhead valve parrallel twin, bore and stroke 76 x 82mm, 5-speed close-ratio Quaife gearbox, Dunstall twin-disc front brake, Norton Dominator rear brake.
£4,500–5,000 *OxM*

1965 Triton 750cc, Morgo engine converted to 750cc, V5 document, good condition.
£2,200–2,400 *PS*

c1960 Triton 650 649cc, pre-unit engine, wide-line frame.
£5,000–5,500 *AtMC*

The classic combination of Triumph and Norton motorcycles.

1969 Norton Mercury 646cc Café Racer Conversion, very good condition.
£3,000–3,600 *BLM*

Last of Featherbed frames before total replacement by Isolastic Commando type.

1956 Norton International/Manx 490cc, International engine, manx Featherbed rolling chassis, good condition.
Est. £7,000–8,000 *BKS*

c1970 Hagon 247cc Grass Track, BSA C15 overhead valve engine, 4-speed gearbox, in good running order.
Est. £350–380 *S*

1957 Norton 99 596cc Café Racer, sweptback pipes, 5-gallon tank, racing seat, clip-ons, alloy rims.
£1,800–2,000 *PM*

1955 Norton 646cc Café Racer, early wide-line frame with engine converted to later 650 configuration.
£2,400–2,800 *ADT*

1975 Triumph Legend 740cc, improved braking, dual seat.
£7,500–8,000 *TOC*

Trident engined special with smooth styling and uprated specification

1981 Harris Magnum 2 998cc, GS 1000 Suzuki engine, Marzocchi forks, twin headlamp fairing, good condition.
£3,000–3,500 *PC*

1960 Triton Wide-Line 649cc, alloy wheel rims, T110 pre-unit motor, TR6 cylinder head, Amal concentric carburettor, Norton gearbox, Thunderbird primary cases, unusual exhaust pipes.
£3,500–4,000 *BLM*

1979 Suzuki Moto Martin GT 750 738cc Café Racer, 3 cylinders, 2-stroke, full body kit expansion chamber exhaust, spider web cast alloy wheels, triple disc brakes.
£1,000–1,200 *MAY*

1956 Norvin 1150cc Special, Vincent engine, Manx Norton cycle parts.
£7,000–9,000 *VMCC*

The Vincent engine has been increased from 998cc to 1150cc. The ultimate special of the classic period, the Norvin combines what is widely regarded as the best engine and the best cycle parts.

1960 Norton Triton 649cc, pre-unit 6T engine, slimline Norton chassis, Norton Featherbed frame, mechanically sound.
Est. £2,300–2,500 *BKS*

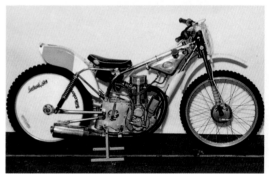

1970s Godden Mark V Grasstrack 500cc, single cyclinder, 4 valves.
£480–520 *PS*

1965 Triton 750cc Racer, T110 engine with Morgo 750 conversion, wide-line frame with 'lowboy' seat rails, 2LS front brake, fully rebuilt, concours condition.
£5,000–5,500 *CBG*

1956 Triton 499cc Special, overhead valve, twin cylinder, Norton Featherbed frame, very good condition, V5 document.
£2,200–2,500 *PS*

1932 Ariel 4F/600 Suare Four 601cc Combination, new oil pump, horn and wiring loom, Doherty pattern handlebars, engine completely rebuilt to as new condition.
Est. £6,000–7,000 *S*

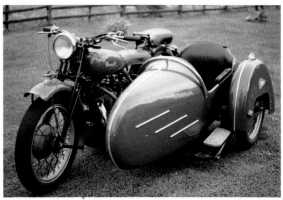

1939 Benelli 500 Single 498cc, overhead camshaft, Longhi sidecar, good condition.
£2,500–3,000 *PC*

1953 BSA M21 596cc, Swallow Jet 80 single seater sidecar, matching red and black finish, good condition.
£1,500–2,000 *BLM*

1931 Harley-Davidson Model U 1200cc Combination, V-twin engine, 3-speed gearbox, factory-fitted sidecar, good condition.
£5,200–5,800 *BKS*

1912 New Hudson Mark VII 3½hp, original sidecar, footboards, and gas lighting.
£8,000–10,000 *VMCC*

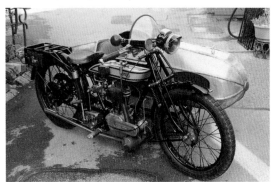

1925 Norton 16H/STEIB 490cc and Sidecar, single valve combination.
£6,000–7,000 *VER*

1921 Matchless Model H 998cc Combination, V-twin, Swiss MAG engine, extensively restored, V5 document, very good condition.
£6,200–6,800 *BKS*

1912 Rover 490cc 3½hp and Combination Wicker Canoelet Sidecar, good condition.
£6,500–7,500 *VER*

1948 Corgi Scooter 98cc, originally built for the RAF, lightweight with handlebars that folded down on the tank, fitted with lighting equipment and in working order.
£500–550 *BKS*

1956 Lambretta 150D 150cc, early Lambretta model.
£2,000–2,500 *CRC*

1957 NSU Prima D 146cc, 2-stroke.
£250–300 *PS*
In 1956 NSU built their own version of a Lambretta called Prima after the Lambretta licence had expired.

1959 Lambretta Li 150 Series 1 147cc.
£800–850 *MAY*

c1959 Triumph Tina 100cc, 2-stroke, equipment includes a luggage/parcel rack and windshield, mechanics and electrics in excellent condition, and paintwork good.
£350–400 *BKS*

1962 BSA Sunbeam 249cc, 4-stroke, twin engine, concours condition.
£1,000–1,400 *CRC*

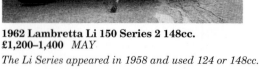

1962 Lambretta Li 150 Series 2 148cc.
£1,200–1,400 *MAY*

The Li Series appeared in 1958 and used 124 or 148cc.

1967 Lambretta SX200 199cc.
£1,400–1,600 *MAY*

Lambretta introduced this scooter to try to combat the decline in sales after 1962.

**A Bolton Social Riders'
Club cast brass badge,**
with painted bike and
background, c1968.
£35–45 *CARS*

**A 'D' Approved Tyre Service Enamel
Sign,** c1960, 23¼in (59cm) diam.
£40–50 *CRC*

Paperotto, by Domenico Laganà,
a sculpture in the form of a duck,
fabricated from Ducati motorcycle
engine and cycle pedals, mounted on
a clutch plate base, 16in (40.5cm) high.
Est. £1,800–2,200 *C*

l. **A Pratt's
Motor Oil
Enamel Sign,**
c1920, some
chips and rust.
£120–140 *MAY*

A BMW Lighting Rear View Mirror,
finished in chrome, 1960s.
£80–100 *ATF*

**An RAC Motorcyclist's
Members' Badge,** in nickel
plated brass, with enamelled
glass Union flag motif, c1925.
£150–175 *CARS*

**An Avery-Hardol
Electric Two-sided
Petrol Pump,** with
Cleveland globe, c1960,
77¼in (196cm) high.
£750–1,250 *CRC*

A Shell X-100 Oil Stand,
c1935, 20½in (52cm) high.
£100–200 *CRC*

A Matchless Dealer Service Enamel Sign,
c1950, 16in (40.5cm) wide.
£45–50 *CRC*

Roxy, by Roy Barrett, watercolour,
17½ x 28in (44.5 x 71cm).
£850–1,000 *ROY*

Wayne's World, by Rod Organ, oil on canvas,
with Wayne Rainey, winning his 3rd 500cc world
title in South Africa, 1992, 24 x 36in (61 x 91.5cm).
£1,000–1,300 *Rod*

A *Rudge* Brochure, 1935,
6½ x 9½in (16.5 x 24cm).
20–25 *DM*

A *BSA* brochure, 1964,
8 x 10in (20.5 x 25.4cm).
£15–20 *DM*

A *Motorcycle Book for Boys,*
published by Iliffe & Sons, London, c1920.
£25–30 *MR*

A *Sun Lightweight Motorcycles* sign,
1953, 7 x 9in (18 x 23cm).
£8–10 *DM*

A *Velocette* brochure, 1931,
7½ x 10in (19 x 25.5cm).
£20–25 *DM*

**Barry Sheene and Kenny Roberts,
Silverstone 1979, by Rod Organ,**
oil on canvas, 20 x 30in (51 x 76cm).
£800–1,100 *Rod*

SUZUKI *(Japanese 1952–)*

Suzuki's origins stem from the year 1909 when Michio Suzuki, its young and aspiring founder, created the Suzuki Loom Company in Hamamatsu, Japan. Business prospered as Suzuki supplied weaving looms to the burgeoning Japanese silk industry. In 1937 the decision was taken to diversify and it negotiated with the British Austin car concern to produce the Austin Seven under licence in Japan but the outbreak of war prevented production.

Following the hostilities, pedal cycles became Japan's main means of personal transport. Following the lead set by Soichiro Honda, a number of companies began to offer small 'clip-on' petrol engines which could be attached to the customer's own bicycle.

Suzuki followed this trend in 1952 by offering a micro-engine which was effectively the launch pad for the Hamamatsu marque's future. Within a year the Power Free was succeeded by the 60cc Diamond Free, the larger engine helping it to cope with Japan's mountainous provincial roads.

In 1954, Suzuki announced their first real motorcycle, the 90cc Colleda, which was also their first 4-stroke. Then followed a myriad of models which featured both 4-stroke and 2-stroke engines from the 50cc Selped moped to the 250cc Colleda twin. Besides motorcycles Suzuki also built cars from the mid-1950s, the first examples being powered by a small capacity 2-stroke engine. Although Suzuki was becoming a force to be reckoned with in the home market, they were all but unknown outside Japan.

Following once again in Honda's footsteps, Suzuki entered a team in the 1960 TT. Success was not immediate, but after the East German Ernst Degner defected at the end of 1961, Suzuki quickly moved to obtain his riding skills and technical knowledge. The result was the Company's first world crown, the 1962 50cc series.

Track success led to showroom sales and soon a never ending array of new models began to flood the export markets of the world, the highlights being the T20 (1966), T500 (1968), GT750 (1971), GS750 (1978), GSX1100 (1981), RG250 (1983), GSXR750 (1984) and RGV250 (1989).

1972 Suzuki T350J Rebel 347cc, distinguishable from earlier T350 with its larger 3.8 gallon tank.
£500–550 *PC*

1976 Suzuki GT380A 371cc, 3 cylinder, air-cooled, 2-stroke, with 'Ram Arm' cylinder heads.
£500–550 *PS*

1978 Suzuki SP370 Racer 369cc.
£700–800 *PC*

One of a small number of machines converted for racing by Vic Camp and later by Alf Hagon.

c1972 Suzuki GT750 738cc.
£2,500–3,000 *AtMC*

1977 Suzuki GT750 738cc, 3 cylinder, 2-stroke, water-cooled, non-standard exhaust.
Est. £2,000–2,500 *BKS*

This was Suzuki's first production water-cooled motorcycle.

1980 Suzuki GS500E 500cc, 2 cylinder, double overhead camshaft.
£450–550 *PS*

Italian model not imported into the UK.

1981 Suzuki GSX1100 Early Stock Racer 1075cc.
£1,800–1,900 *PC*

Developed from the original GS750, the GSX1100 (and 750) were performance setters in their day, the larger version making 100bhp at 8700rpm.

1983 Suzuki GSX250 249cc, double overhead camshaft, twin cylinder, 6-speed gearbox.
£300–350 *PS*

Suzuki's first 250 4-stroke, which was manufactured in 1978.

1984 Suzuki RG250 247cc.
£900–950 *PC*

This machine marked the switch from air-cooled to liquid cooled engines in the sports roadster field.

1984 Suzuki TGA1-500 Solo Racing 500cc, engine is works Suzuki GXR40 Square Four, 2-stroke, 140bhp at 11000rpm.
Est. £20,000–25,000 *S*

Developed from the RG500 of the 1970s, the TGA-1 was the work of Massimo Tamburini and Roberta Gallina.

1985 Suzuki GSXR750 749cc, 16-valve engine, concours condition.
£3,000–3,500 *PC*

Developed from the Company's participation in endurance racing.

1985 Suzuki Sacs, unregistered.
£850–900 *BKS*

A Japanese import based on the popular mini bike of the 1970s.

TERROT
(French 1901–early 1960s)

1922 Terrot 238cc, good original condition.
£2,000–2,500 *S*

c1923 Terrot 300cc.
£3,500–4,000 *AtMC*

TRIUMPH (British 1902–)
Pre-war Speed Twin Profile

Edward Turner unwittingly earned himself fame and immortality after he joined Triumph as chief designer in 1936 when he conceived the half-litre parallel twin engine which made its debut late the following year in the first Speed Twin. Over 20 years earlier WWI had ended Triumph's hopes of building their first parallel twin, a 600cc side valve job. Their second effort, designed by Val Page, was also a failure in 1932. This was a semi-unit construction 633cc 4-speed engine with double helical primary drive and one-piece crank which ran backwards. Its robustness was proven by Harry Perrey who won a sidecar 'gold' in the 1933 ISDT. Its only problem was bulk and cost. These two failings transpired to kill it off, and only 40 were made.

In 1936 Edward Turner left Ariel where he had designed the Square Four. On joining Triumph, he set about designing a parallel twin. His initial layout included an OHC engine, but this was abandoned in favour of a more simple push-rod unit which was pleasingly symmetrical. This had identical dimensions (63 x 80mm) to the 250 single then being built by Triumph, so production could be rationalised with pistons, small ends, rings and circlips being common parts. An iron head and barrel was fitted, the latter with a 6 stud base flange which was changed to an 8 stud unit in 1939 after some had cracked. The connecting rods were of forged RR56 aluminium alloy with inserted steel caps lined with white metal big end shells. There were full skirt pistons, gear drive cams, dural pushrods, forged rockers and bolt-on rocker boxes. Behind the cylinder sat a magdyno driven from the inlet cam while a peg on the end of the shaft drove a double plunger oil pump. In prototype form the engine produced 30bhp, while the initial production models of 1937 gave 3 or 4bhp less, but still good enough to provide 90mph top speed. Compared to the single cylinder bikes of the day, the Speed Twin was practicable, flexible, quieter and easier to start. Triumph were on to a winner.

In its amaranth red livery the 1938 Speed Twins were snapped up like hot cakes. This success was influential in other manufacturers following the trend over the next 3 decades. In fact, the parallel twin concept held through to 1969 when Honda launched its trend setting 750-4 ushering in the era of the Superbike.

1908 Triumph 3½hp 499cc,
£4,500–4,800 *S*

1909 Triumph 500cc, single cylinder, good overall condition.
£4,000–4,500 *BKS*

1911 Triumph 500cc, belt final drive, still in use.
£7,000–7,500 *TOC*

c1913 Triumph 3½hp.
Est. £3,400–3,800 *BKS*

The first Triumph motorcycle of 1902 used a Belgian Minerva engine, but within a few years the Coventry firm (originally bicycle manufacturers) was building its own power units. By the outbreak of the Great War the marque's reputation for quality and reliability was well-established and led to substantial orders for 'Trusty Triumphs' for British and Allied forces. The 3½hp model first appeared in 1907. Originally of 453cc, its side valve engine was enlarged to 476cc in 1908, and finally to 499cc in 1910 before being superseded by the 4hp model in 1914.

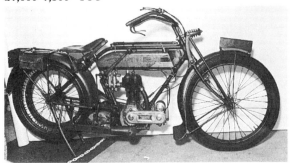

1919 Triumph Model H 550cc, unrestored, poor condition.
£1,800–2,000 *PVE*
Made popular as WWI despatch rider's bike.

1923 Triumph 500cc, side valve, single cylinder, in good condition.
£3,500–3,800 *BKS*

1924 Triumph 550cc, side valve.
£2,250–2,750 *PM*

1924 Triumph Model LW Junior 249cc.
£1,800–2,000 *BKS*

Introduced shortly before the Great War, Triumph's Lightweight (LW) Junior model was reintroduced in 1919 and proved popular, remaining in production until 1925. It featured a 249cc single cylinder 2-stroke engine, distinctive round tank and 2-speed countershaft gearbox with chain-cum-belt drive.

1925 Triumph Model P 500cc.
£2,000–2,200 *BLM*

1926 Triumph Model P 500cc.
£2,000–2,200 *BLM*

1926 Triumph Model Q 495cc.
£2,500–2,800 *BKS*

The Q was a sportier version of the popular Model H Triumph.

1934 Triumph L21 Grass Track 249cc.
£3,200–3,400 *BKS*

This bike is an historic racer with numerous wins at Worcester Grass Track, Wroughton, Bridgnorth, Birmingham and Coventry.

1927 Triumph Model QA 494cc, side valve, in good mechanical condition.
£3,400–3,600 *BKS*

1937 Triumph 3S 343cc, single cylinder, side valve.
£2,500–2,800 *BKS*

c1938 Triumph 3HW 343cc, single cylinder, overhead valve, export model, restoration needed.
£700–800 *BKS*

1938 Triumph Speed Twin 498cc, overhead
valve, in excellent condition.
Est. £3,500–4,000 *BKS*

*Up until 1936 the Triumph plant at Coventry
produced cars, motorcycles and pedal cycles. The
management at that time decided its future lay with
cars and planned to drop the motorcycle production
side of its business. Ariel boss, Jack Sangster heard
of these plans and a deal was made to retain an
option on part of the works to continue motorcycle
production. He appointed Edward Turner to run the
enterprise and it was he who designed a new vertical
twin for the Triumph name announced in 1937 as
the Model T, soon to adopt the name Speed Twin
and a catalogue listing 5T.*

1939 Triumph Tiger 100 499cc, as new condition.
£6,000–7,000 *HH*

*First year of sports version of the famous Speed
Twin. Pre-war models are now rare.*

1944 Triumph 3HW 350cc, overhead valve.
£1,200–1,400 *AT*
Civilianised WWII machine.

l. **1947 Triumph Tiger 100 499cc,** optional
sprung hub model, period panniers fitted.
£3,250–3,500 *BKS*

1946 Triumph 3T De Luxe 349cc, overhead
valve, telescopic forks, rigid frame.
£1,250–1,450 *BKS*

Early post-war model.

1949 Triumph TR5 Trophy 499cc, square alloy
barrelled engine, rigid frame, competition model
with QD lighting set.
£4,500–5,000 *FMC*

1949 Triumph Thunderbird 649cc.
Est. £4,500–5,000 *BKS*

Always a step ahead of their rivals, Triumph followed up the trend-setting Speed Twin 500 of pre-war days by being first in the field with a 650 parallel twin. Announced in September 1949, the 650 Thunderbird was Triumph's response to demands for more power emanating from American racers and British sidecarists. A spectacular launch stunt saw 3 Thunderbirds lap the Monthery circuit at over 90mph for 500 miles, after which they each achieved a flying lap of 100mph-plus, and were ridden back to the Meriden factory. When displayed at the Earls Court Show in October, the new twin featured the headlamp nacelle and fuel tank with luggage grid first seen the previous year.

1951 Triumph TR5 Trophy 499cc.
£3,400–3,600 *COYS*

ISDT replica as offered by Triumph.

1952 Triumph 100 499cc, sprung hub model, tank top grill, alloy rims.
£1,800–2,000 *PS*

1952 Triumph Tiger 100 499cc, overhead valve, twin cylinder.
£3,000–3,500 *BKS*

1952 was the year a Tiger 100 won the Senior Clubman's TT, ridden by Bernard Hargreaves.

1949 Triumph 5T Speed Twin 499cc, overhead valve, headlamp nacelle, optional sprung hub fitted, limited amount of rear wheel movement.
£3,000–3,500 *S*

1949 Triumph TRW 498cc, twin cylinder, side valve.
Est. £1,700–1,800 *BKS*

Ex-military model.

1951 Triumph 6T Thunderbird 650cc, overhead valve, twin cylinder, sprung hub rear suspension.
£3,800–4,250 *AT*

1952 Triumph Thunderbird 6T 649cc, MkII sprung hub.
£2,500–3,000 *BLM*

For 1952 the 6T was fitted with an SU carburettor. The MkII sprung hub had first appeared for the 1950 season.

1953 Triumph TRW 500cc, side valve.
£1,000–1,300 *BLM*

Ex-display team bike.

1955 Triumph TR5 Trophy 499cc, overhead valve, twin cylinder.
£3,500–4,000 *COYS*

1955 model saw the sprung hub replaced by swinging arm and power rise to 33bhp.

1956 Triumph Thunderbird 649cc, concours, fully restored to original condition.
£5,500–6,000 *ARE*

1956 Triumph Tiger 110 649cc, TR6 USA model exhaust, poor non-original condition.
£800–850 *BLM*

1956 Triumph T100 Tiger 499cc, twin cylinder, Roddark panniers.
£3,000–4,000 *CRC*

1957 Triumph Tiger 100 499cc, splayed inlet ports, twin carburettors, large ventilated front brake.
£3,250–3,750 *BLM*

1958 Triumph 5T 499cc, good overall condition.
£2,000–2,500 *BKS*

1958 Triumph TR5 Trophy 499cc, overhead valve, full width front hub, siamesed exhaust.
£3,250–3,500 *COYS*

1958 Triumph T20C Trials 199cc, lightweight, 4-stroke.
£1,000–1,250 *BLM*

Trials conversion of T20C. The pukka TR20 did not appear until 1962.

r. **1959 Triumph T120 649cc.**
£5,750–6,000 *BKS*

The most prestigious named machine to emerge from Meriden was the Bonneville 120 or T120 for short. It appeared upon the 1958 Earls Court Triumph stand and arrived too late to be included in the 1959 catalogue.

1959 Triumph Tiger Cub 199cc.
£420–480 *BKS*

The Tiger Cub was first introduced in 1954 as a bigger brother to the 150cc Terrier, which appeared in 1953. The Triumph factory had introduced lightweight machines into its range in the years 1913, 1933 and 1953 but it was the Cub which probably eclipsed all previous lightweight models. It remained in production until 1968. Probably one of the most astonishing feats accomplished by a Cub was by an American who, using a Cub as the basis for a new American Motorcycle Association speed record over a measured mile, achieved a one-way speed of 149.31mph (240.28kph).

1959 Triumph Tiger 100 499cc, high performance twin carburettor model.
£2,500–3,000 *BLM*

1959 Triumph Twenty-One 349cc, original condition.
£1,300–1,500 *BKS*

Early in 1957 Triumph announced a new model called the Twenty-One to celebrate the twenty-first birthday of the Triumph Engineering Co and the useful fact that in the USA a 350cc engine falls in the 21cu in class.

1960 Triumph Tiger Cub T20 199cc.
£700–750 *PM*

1959 Triumph 3TA Trials 349cc, overhead valve, twin cylinder.
£900–1,000 *BKS*

1959 Triumph T100 500cc, all alloy engine, good original condition.
£3,000–3,200 *AT*

1959 Triumph Tiger 100 499cc, original except later 2LS front brake.
£2,550–2,750 *PM*

The pre-unit T100 was discontinued in June 1959, being replaced the following year by the unit construction T100A.

1960 Triumph T120 Bonneville 649cc, pre-unit motor, duplex frame.
£4,500–5,000 *BLM*

Flagship of the Triumph range the T120 Bonneville lost its nacelle for 1960 when it gained a new frame and alternator.

1960 Triumph T110 649cc, V-twin, overhead valve, T110 converted to TR6 specification.
£2,200–2,400 *PS*

c1960 Triumph Daytona Spec. Racer 490cc,
5 gallon tank, 2LS front brake, alloy rims, fly
screen, rearseats, racing exhaust.
£850–900 *BKS*

1960 Triumph T110 649cc, converted to
look like T120 Bonneville.
£2,000–2,500 *BLM*

1961 Triumph T120R 649cc, tacho drive, 3 gallon
tank, modified head angle, floating brake shoes.
£4,000–4,500 *PM*

1961 Triumph T110 649cc, lacking
bathtub, valanced front mudguard, non-
standard chrome oil tank, custom dual seat,
pattern silencers.
£1,250–1,500 *BKS*

1961 Triumph 6T 649cc, pre-unit, duplex frame.
£3,000–3,200 *BLM*

*Originally a 6T Thunderbird with bathtub and
converted to Bonneville specification.*

1960 Triumph Tiger Cub T20 199cc, 4-stroke,
rear half enclosure missing, good clean condition.
£850–900 *BLM*

1960 Triumph T20 Tiger Cub 199cc, overhead
valve, single cylinder with unit construction.
£680–720 *BKS*

1961 Triumph Twenty-One 349cc.
£1,500–2,000 *MAY*

Actual machine used in TV Heartbeat series.

1961 Triumph T100A 490cc, missing original
bodywork, looking like later T100SS post-1963 model.
£1,750–2,000 *BKS*

1961 Triumph T110 649cc, overhead valve,
twin cylinder.
Est. £3,200–3,400 *BKS*

*In 1960 the T110 (and 6T) were fitted with
bathtub rear enclosure and valenced front
mudguard. This did not prove popular and
the T110 was discontinued in August 1961.
Conversely the bathtub models have become
collectable in the classic boom of the 1980s
and 1990s.*

1962 Triumph T20 Tiger Cub, 4-stroke, semi-bathtub.
£650–750 *CRC*

1963 Triumph 3TA 350cc, missing original mudguards and bathtub enclosure.
£1,000–1,200 *BLM*

1964 Triumph T120 Bonneville 649cc, excellent condition mechanically.
£3,500–4,800 *BKS*

The first unit construction Bonneville appeared the previous year in 1963.

1964 Triumph Twenty-One, half bathtub, gold livery, concours condition.
£1,500–2,000 *TOC*

1965 Triumph Tiger 90 349cc.
£1,000–1,500 *PM*

T90 (and T100SS) had new forks for 1965.

1963 Triumph Bonneville 649cc, overhead valve, twin cylinder, unit construction, concours condition.
Est. £4,000–4,500 *BKS*

1963 Triumph 6T Thunderbird 649cc, half 'bath tub' rear end, 2-tone seat, immaculate and original specification.
£3,000–3,500 *BLM*

1964 Triumph TRW 500cc, side valve, twin cylinder, original army trim, army release papers.
£1,000–1,500 *AT*

1964 Triumph T120 Bonneville.
£3,000–3,500 *AT*

One of the first unit construction machines.

1965 Triumph T90 349cc.
£1,550–1,850 *PC*

New forks for T90 (and T100) in 1965, separate exhausts came a year earlier, as did deletion of partial rear enclosure.

1966 Triumph Tiger 90 349cc, incorrect front forks, non-standard disc front brake, poor condition.
£700–800 *BLM*

1966 Triumph 3TA Twenty-One 349cc, non-standard BSA front brake, frame changes, 12v electrics.
£900–1,000 *PM*

The 1966 3TA (and larger 5TA) had no partial rear enclosure.

1966 Triumph Tiger 90 349cc, sports version, non-standard colour scheme.
£1,200–1,400 *BLM*

1967 Triumph Tiger 90 349cc.
£1,500–1,750 *PM*

1967 Triumph TR6 Trophy 649cc, American specification, stacked silencers, unit construction.
£2,800–3,200 *S*

1967 Triumph T100T Daytona 490cc, twin carburettors, new head, 8in front brake.
£1,400–1,600 *PS*

First year of T100T Daytona production.

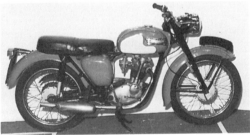

1967 Triumph T20 Super Cub 199cc, Bantam tank, full-width hubs, minor changes.
£600–700 *PS*

This model was axed in 1968.

1967 Triumph T90 349cc, without half bathtub rear enclosure, siamesed exhaust, non-standard alloy rims.
£1,500–1,750 *PC*

1968 Triumph T120 Bonneville 649cc, twin cylinder.
£3,500–4,500 *CRC*

1969 Triumph TR25W.
£1,500–2,000 *BKS*

Badge engineered BSA model.

1969 Triumph T100SS 490cc, 7in 2LS front brake.
£2,000–2,200 *MR*

1969 Triumph TR6P Trophy 649cc,
ex-police machine converted to civilian
specification, fully restored.
£3,250–3,750 *BLM*

c1969 Triumph T120 Bonneville 649cc,
overhead valve, twin cylinder.
£2,750–3,000 *PS*

1970 Triumph TR6 Trophy 649cc,
single carburettor of Bonneville.
£2,400–2,600 *BLM*

1971 Triumph T25SS 247cc.
£600–700 *CStC*

r. **1973 Triumph Daytona T100R 490cc,**
improvements new switches, rubber mounted
instruments, headlamps and indicators.
£2,400–2,600 *BLM*

T100R replaced T100T for 1971.

1969 Triumph Trident T150 740cc,
3 cylinder, overhead valve, 4-speed, drum
brakes, fishtail silencers, BSA style lights and
forks, totally restored.
£2,000–2,500 *COYS*

1969 Triumph TR6 Trophy 649cc, pre-unit
construction, V-twin, overhead valve.
£3,000–3,500 *PS*

1970 Triumph T120 Bonneville 649cc.
Est. £3,800–4,200 *BKS*

*The last Bonneville generation before BSA-Triumph
switched to the Umberslade Hall designed oil-in-
frame model.*

1971 Triumph Trophy Trial 490cc, overhead
valve, twin cylinder.
£2,000–3,000 *CRC*

*Otherwise known as the Adventurer. This was
almost a production version of Triumph's unit 500
ISDT bike.*

1975 Triumph Trident T150V 740cc.
£2,500–3,000 *BLM*

Last of upright engined Tridents before switching to
T160 model with BSA sloping style cylinders.

1978 Triumph Bonneville T140V 744cc, 5-speed
gearbox, left-hand posi-stop change.
£1,800–2,000 *BKS*

1978 Triumph T160 740cc, 3 cylinder,
electric start.
£2,500–3,500 *CRC*

1982 Triumph TSS 744cc.
£2,000–2,500 *S*

By the beginning of the 1980s it was becoming
apparent that Triumph required a machine with
considerably more performance if they were to
remain competitive in the market place. The result
was the TSS, the last of Meriden's designs based
on the original Bonneville. It featured an 8-valve
head on a considerably revised bottom-end.

This was a machine that matched its European
competitors in terms of performance, if not their
Japanese rivals as well. Unfortunately, before the
machine had the opportunity to establish itself on
the market, Triumph had succumbed to their
financial problems.

1977 Triumph Silver Jubilee
Bonneville 744cc.
£3,800–4,200 *S*

Built to commemorate Her Majesty the
Queen's Silver Jubilee in 1977, the special
edition Bonnevilles feature a silver finish
lined with red, white and blue, chrome
primary and timing side covers and Girling
gas shocks.

This machine is one of the 1,000 allocated
for sale in this country, a further 1,400
being built for the rest of the world.

1980 Triumph Tiger Trail 750cc,
upswept exhaust, braced handlebars, dual
purpose tyres and plastic mudguards.
£3,250–4,000 *S*

Launched at the 1980 Paris Show.

1981 Triumph Tiger Trail 744cc.
Est. £3,500–3,800 *BKS*

Only 208 examples of the Tiger Trail were
built, most being exported to Europe.

1990 Triumph Buccaneer 744cc.
Est. £4,550–5,000 *BKS*

Based on a 1978 Triumph T140 Bonneville, this
machine comes with its original invoice from the
builder, L. P. Williams, and differs from the
specification of the original donor bike. It is one of
a limited series built by Les Williams, the owner
of the famous ex-works racer 'Slippery Sam'. It is
Serial No. 010 (ten) and has completed only 1000
miles since being rebuilt.

VELOCETTE (British 1904–68)
LE – The Noddy Bike – Profile

When Veloce Ltd, makers of Velocette motorcycles, announced in October 1948 their LE model (the initials stood for Little Engine), the bike-buying public could scarcely have received a bigger shock. To most enthusiasts Velocette meant big meaty singles such as the K Series overhead cam sportsters plus the 350 MAC and 500 MSS; there had also been the 2-stroke GTP in pre-war days. But the newcomer was something totally out of character. Of only 149cc, an increase to 192cc coming later, the LE was a transverse water-cooled flat twin side valve, with integral gearbox and shaft final drive, mounted in a substantial pressed steel frame.

Designed by Charles Udall, it displayed much original thought. The final drive shaft, for example, was housed within the nearside leg of the cast alloy rear-pivoted fork, and the upper ends of the rear spring units could be moved through slotted upper mountings in the rear mudguard pressing, to allow for variation in the load-carrying capacity of the machine. Instead of a conventional kickstart, starting was achieved by the use of a long lever on the offside, initial movement of which released then raised the centre stand. For ease of maintenance, the entire subframe comprising engine/gearbox assembly, radiator, rear fork and wheel could be detached readily from the main frame member.

Strangely, as Velocette had invented the positive stop gearchange, a hand change lever was a feature of the LE, this operating in a car-type gate. Other features of note included deeply valenced mudguards, footboards and comprehensive aluminium leg shields.

Sales never reached expectations even though the LE was to become a familiar sight on British roads through police use, hence its 'Noddy Bike' title. In fact the LE, together with the Valiant, Vogue and Viceroy scooter, only served to hasten the ultimate decline, and subsequent extinction, of Velocette.

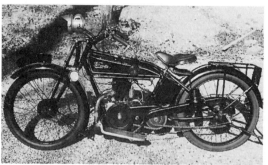

1925 Velocette G 249cc, single cylinder, 2-stroke engine, 3-speed gearbox, girder forks, rigid frame, rear carrier, footboards.
£3,000–3,500 *VER*

1931 Velocette GTP 250cc, 2-stroke, good condition.
£1,800–2,000 *AT*

Miller's is a price GUIDE not a price LIST

1934 Velocette KTS 348cc, overhead camshaft.
£4,000–4,500 *Vel*

From 1932 the KTP was replaced by the superior KTS which was simply a KSS with touring credentials.

1934 Velocette KSS MkI 348cc, overhead camshaft.
£2,600–3,000 *BKS*

Introduced in 1925, the Velocette KSS was the super sports version of Veloce Ltd's first post-WWI 4-stroke, the overhead camshaft Model K. Along with the other K models, the 90mph KSS was offered with the revolutionary positive-stop foot-controlled gear change devised by the company's development engineer, Harold Willis, from 1929.

1935 Velocette KTT MkV 348cc Racer, overhead camshaft, square ML magneto rebuilt 3 years ago, the gearbox, frame, and mechanics in good condition.
£7,500–8,000 *BKS*

This KTT was originally supplied to Billy Tiffin Jnr, for the 1935 Junior TT.

1935 Velocette KSS MkII 348cc, overhead
camshaft single, good condition, V5.
£4,500–5,000 *BKS*

1936 Velocette KTS 348cc, overhead camshaft,
alloy cylinder head, enclosed valve gear,
requires restoration.
Est. £4,000–6,000 *BKS*

*The Velocette KTS tourer employed the same
overhead camshaft engine as the Hall Green factory's
renowned KSS sports machine. The cycle parts used
for both models were similar, the differences being
confined mainly to mudguard style and wheel sizes.*

1936 Velocette Model MOV 248cc,
overhead valve, speedometer, full
electric lighting set, pillion seat and
fish tail silencer, original, good
condition throughout, Swansea V5.
£2,000–2,200 *BKS*

*The smallest of Velocette's high cam
singles, the MOV was announced in
June 1933. Its nearly square engine,
68 x 68.25mm, gave it the ability to rev
and also accept considerable tuning, to
the extent that racing MOVs were good
for 100mph.*

c1937 Velocette MSS 499cc.
£4,500–5,000 *AtMC*

1938 Velocette KSS MkII 348cc,
overhead camshaft, single.
£4,000–4,500 *Vel*

1938 Velocette MAC 349cc,
overhead valve single, girder forks,
rigid frame, Brooklands 'can' silencer.
£2,500–3,000 *BLM*

c1939 Velocette GTP 249cc.
£3,500–4,000 *AtMC*

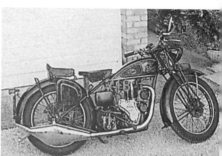

1939 Velocette MAC 349cc, overhead valve single, sports mudguards, good original condition throughout.
£1,500–2,000 *C*

The MAC was basically a long stroke version of the 248cc MOV. It was priced around £50 when new with a speed of 70mph.

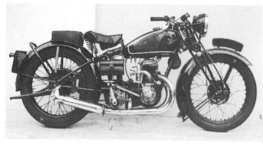

1939 Velocette GTP 249cc.
£2,000–3,000 *VER*

The GTP replaced the P model Velocette 2-stroke for the 1930 model. Late in 1934 a 4-speed gearbox replaced the original 3-speed one, otherwise there were remarkably few changes between the 1930 and 1939 shown here.

1939 Velocette GTP 250cc, 2-stroke, good condition.
£2,000–2,200 *AT*

1947 Velocette KSS MkII 348cc, overhead camshaft single.
£2,700–3,000 *BKS*

The engine of the KSS was a major item, distinguishing it from its more mundane overhead valve brothers; the wheels also differed, being 21in (53.5cm) front and 20in (51cm) rear.

1948 Velocette KSS MkII 348cc, overhead camshaft, Dowty front fork, non-standard petrol tank, professional mechanical rebuild, Swansea V5.
Est. £3,500–4,000 *S*

This machine was built in the final year of production for the overhead cam KSS model.

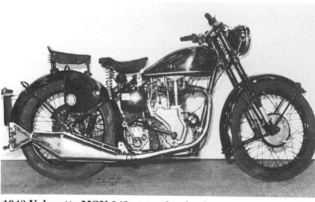

1948 Velocette MOV 248cc, overhead valve.
£1,300–1,800 *PS*

Built in the final year of manufacture of this model.

1948 Velocette MAC 349cc, overhead valve single, rigid frame, telescopic front forks.
£2,400–2,500 *BLM*

The MAC, together with the 248cc MOV and 499cc MSS all had their roots in the 1930s. All were similar in engine layout, with the camshaft set high up in the timing side, where it was driven by helical gears, which also drove the magneto.

1951 Velocette MAC 349cc, overhead valve.
£3,000–3,200 *Vel*

1952 Velocette MAC 349cc, overhead valve,
rigid frame, non-standard exhaust, alloy rims.
£1,400–1,700 *MAY*

1954 Velocette LE MkII 192cc.
£900–1,000 *LEV*

1954 Velocette MSS 499cc, overhead
valve, excellent condition.
£3,500–3,800 *BKS*

This is the actual road test bike used by
Classic Bike *magazine in 1979.*

1955 Velocette MSS 499cc, original rebuilt engine,
mechanically excellent, good overall condition.
£3,000–4,000 *SW*

1955 Velocette MAC 349cc, fitted with later seat,
of the type introduced with the Viper/Venom in
1956, otherwise in original concours condition.
£2,700–3,000 *BLM*

1956 Velocette Venom 499cc, air-cooled,
overhead valve single, air-cooled.
£2,500–3,000 *BKS*

*The Venom, and 349cc Viper, were launched
in 1956. Both did much to carry Velocette into
the 1960s.*

1957 Velocette Venom 499cc,
overhead valve single.
£2,500–3,000 *BLM*

*Cheaper Clubman version, but with its
original engine cowlings dispensed with.*

> **Miller's is a price GUIDE
> not a price LIST**

l. **1958 Velocette LE 192cc,** water-cooled twin
cylinder, side valve.
£750–1,200 *CRC*

1958 Velocette LE 192cc, water-cooled flat twin, in
need of restoration.
£250–300 *AT*

1959 Velocette Valiant 192cc, air-cooled, overhead
valve, flat twin engine, based on
water-cooled side valve LE unit.
£1,200–1,500 *LEV*

1960 Velocette Valiant 192cc, alloy wheel
rims, otherwise original concours condition.
£1,200–1,500 *LEV*

1961 Velocette MAC 349cc, single cylinder
overhead valve, fish tail exhaust.
£2,000–3,000 *CRC*

1962 Velocette LE 192cc, water-cooled,
transversely mounted engine with gearbox
in unit, original in all major respects,
needs recommissioning.
£750–1,000 *BKS*

1959 Velocette Venom 499cc.
£3,000–4,000 *Vel*

*This version of the Venom was launched in 1959,
featuring cowlings for the bottom half of the
engine unit. The idea behind this was a cleaner
motorcycle, allowing the company to save the
expense of polishing the bottom engine covers.*

1959 Velocette MAC 349cc, overhead valve,
non-standard polished alloy mudguards, chrome
headlamp brackets, overall good condition, V5.
£1,500–1,800 *BKS*

1961 Velocette Venom Clubman 499cc,
overhead valve single, Thruxton-type saddle,
non-standard alloy guards.
£2,500–3,000 *BLM*

1960 Velocette Valiant 192cc, air-cooled,
overhead valve flat twin, Dunstall reverse cone
silencers, tubular cradle frame, good condition
throughout, Swansea V5.
£400–600 *BKS*

*Derived from the LE, production of the Valiant
ceased in 1964.*

1962 Velocette LE 192cc, well preserved and original condition, 12 volt electrical system, with spare 6 volt generator, Swansea V5.
£550–800 *S*

Although originally intended as a motorcycle for the general public, it was with the police that the LE found its greatest popularity. It offered policemen on the beat an almost silent means of transport, and was considerably quicker than the bicycle.

1964 Velocette Venom 500cc, excellent condition.
£3,000–3,250 *AT*

1967 Velocette Thruxton 499cc, tuned engine, Amal GP carburettor, clip-on handlebars, rear set footrests, twin leading-shoe front brake.
£6,000–7,000 *BKS*

Production race successes, notably in the Thruxton 500 Mile event, prompted Veloce Ltd to adopt the name for their newly introduced top-of-the-range sports single in 1964. Although much admired by the café racing fraternity, the Thuxton's high price limited its appeal. It is thought that as few as 1,000 were produced.

1972 Velocette Venom Metisse 499cc Racer, Rickman Metisse chassis, tuned Venom engine, Grimeca front brake, nickel-plated frame, finished in British Racing green, CRMC registered.
£3,500–4,000 *CRMC*

1964 Velocette MSS Scrambler 499cc, good overall condition, new mudguards, no known modifications from original specification.
£4,500–5,000 *BKS*

Although relatively few Scramblers were made production ran from 1955 to 1968. This particular machine was part of the Rochester Motorcycle Museum, assembled by Ken and Michael Bills, until the early 1990s.

1965 Velocette Venom VeeLine 499cc.
£2,500–3,500 *CRC*

1968 Velocette Vogue 192cc.
£1,800–2,000 *LEV*

When new the Vogue was a sales flop, but now examples are rare and very collectable compared to the LE and Valiant models.

VILLA *(Italian 1968–)*

1968 Villa 50cc Racing.
£550–650 *BKS*

The Villa brothers produced a line of racing models which began with 50 and 65cc machines. This is one of the earliest, with a Minerelli engine.

VINCENT-HRD *(British 1924–55)*

D Series Profile

At the 1954 Earls Court Show the Stevenage based Vincent concern displayed three all-enclosed models for the new season. These were the 499cc Victor single, 998cc Black Knight and Black Prince V-twins, replacing respectively the familiar Comet, Rapide and Black Shadow models. History shows that the Victor never made it to production and only one prototype was constructed.

At Earls Court the newcomers attracted comment in plenty – unfortunately for the company not all favourable. Much of this was due to the British motorcyclist being conservative in nature and existing Vincent owners in particular considering it sacrilege to hide the beautiful machinery of a Vincent engine behind an anonymous sheet of plastic.

Factory owner Philip Vincent was also burdened with the fact that manufacture of the glass fibre mouldings had to be undertaken by an outside supplier, whose workmanship left much to be desired. The result was that whilst another contractor was sought Vincent were forced to produce an unclothed Series D range for a while, simply to keep the workforce occupied.

Already in an unstable financial position these problems brought the bike side of the business to its knees, the result being that a mere 460 Vincents of all types were built in 1955. Only 200 of these were the new enclosed type. The very last Vincent to roll off the Great North Road assembly line was a 998cc Black Prince on 16th December 1955, although a few more were constructed subsequently from spare parts.

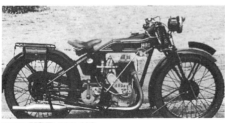

1925 HRD 500 499cc.
£7,500–8,000 *PM*

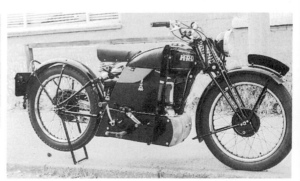

1934 HRD MOD W 499cc.
£7,000–7,500 *AtMC*

1947 Vincent-HRD Series B Rapide 998cc, the subject of a cosmetic restoration, spokes, brake linings, voltage regulator, headlamp and ammeter, dynamo armature and fork links replaced in 1990, generally good mechanical condition, dynamo requires reconnection.
Est. £8,000–10,000 *S*

This example of Vincent-HRD's Series B Rapide was first registered in this country in 1990, having spent the previous 43 years in Argentina.

1947–49 Vincent Series B Rapide 998cc.
£5,800–6,500 *BKS*

Imported recently from Argentina.

> **Miller's is a price GUIDE not a price LIST**

l. **1947–49 Vincent Series B Rapide 998cc,** overhead valve V-twin.
Est. £7,500–9,000 *BKS*

The Vincent factory introduced their new Series B Rapide model to the motorcycle press in early 1946. However, it was another 5 months before the first B Rapide was finished and road-tested and the very next day it was flown to Buenos Aires and exhibited at a trade fair. Phil Vincent had family links with Argentina and as a result of the trade fair orders began to come in from that country. The Rapide was quite a new project for the factory with V-twin unit construction, its famous section frame and Brampton girder forks. A new legend was subsequently born.

1949 Vincent Series B Rapide 998cc.
£6,500–8,000 *BKS*

Phil Vincent had family links with Argentina, his father had emigrated there in the 1880s and in the 1940s his sister had also taken up residence. Opportunities therefore presented themselves to Phil and at one stage the Argentinian Police Force rode B Rapide motorcycles.

1950 Vincent Comet 499cc, overhead valve single.
£4,800–5,200 *BKS*

1951 Vincent Comet 499cc, overhead valve single.
Est. £5,000–5,500 *BKS*

Effectively a Rapide V-twin, minus its rear cylinder, the Series C Vincent Comet built from 1948 to 1954 offered the same degree of refinement as its bigger brother, albeit with reduced performance. Even so, the Comet combined a 90mph potential with excellent fuel economy, and was the ideal touring motorcycle for many discerning riders.

1951 Vincent Comet Series C 499cc, only 617 miles recorded, original showroom condition.
£6,500–7,000 *PC*

l. **1951 Vincent Comet 499cc,** in working condition.
£3,000–3,250 *AT*

1952 Vincent Comet 499cc, overhead valve.
£4,000–4,500 *CStC*

1952 Vincent Black Shadow 998cc, overhead valve V-twin, 12 volt electronic ignition, good original example.
£13,000–14,000 *BKS*

Probably the most famous of the range produced by the Stevenage factory, the Black Shadow was the ultimate big twin of its era. Developed from the Rapide, it received engine modifications to boost its bhp.

1953 Vincent Comet 499cc, overhead valve single, very good condition.
£4,200–4,600 *VER*

1953 Vincent Rapide C 998cc, overhead valve 50° V-twin.
£10,000–11,000 *VER*

1954 Vincent Series C 998cc,
overhead valve V-twin.
£7,700–9,000 *PS*

This machine started life as a 499cc single cylinder Comet model. The Comet engine was later replaced by a 998cc V-twin engine following a complete restoration during which this latter engine was rebuilt completely.

1955 Vincent Black Knight 998cc, overhead valve V-twin.
£11,500–13,000 *BKS*

It was Philip Vincent's belief that provision of ample weather protection, combined with enclosure of engine and gearbox, would make the Vincent Series D the ultimate 'gentleman's motorcycle'. However, delayed delivery of the glass fibre panels plus continuing demand for traditionally-styled models resulted in over half the production leaving the Stevenage factory in un-enclosed form. The enclosed Rapide and Black Shadow were known as Black Knight and Black Prince respectively. Other D Series innovations included a new frame and rear suspension, a user-friendly centre stand, plus many improvements to the engine. But by the time manufacture of Vincent's final range commenced in March 1955, the company was already in financial difficulty. When production ceased in December that year, around 460 Series D V-twins had been built, some 200 of which were enclosed models.

1955 Vincent Black Prince 998cc, V-twin.
£16,000–18,000 *CRC*

r. **1955 Vincent Open Series D Black Shadow 998cc,** overhead valve V-twin, Black Shadow speedo, finned brake drum, Lightning air scoop on front brake, tubular sub-frame, rare.
£12,000–15,000 *BLM*

WANDERER *(German 1902–29)*

Vincent

An interesting aside to the Vincent story was the company's involvement with the German manufacturer NSU. In November 1953, Philip Vincent explained to the gathered press that Anglicised versions of NSU machines would be built at Stevenage for sale in Great Britain and the Commonwealth. Unfortunately, history was to show that this was to be a dismal failure. The sole achievements were the production and sale of a paltry 160 examples of the Fox 2-stroke and the completion of the single 250cc Max prototype.

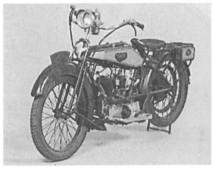

c1919 Wanderer 415cc, side-valve V-twin engine in unit with the gearbox, carrier, tool boxes, footboards, and lighting equipment, complete and original, good condition.
£8,500–9,500 *S*

YAMAHA *(Japan 1954–)*

Yamaha conjures up a sporting image with any motorcycle enthusiast, though if its successes in racing, motocross and trials are combined, both Honda and Suzuki could probably boast as many, if not more, victories.

The reason for this image lies in Yamaha's unwavering commitment to racing since the early 1960s, which included both pukka works machinery and the offering of production 'over-the-counter' bikes for both club and national riders around the world.

The company has also manufactured musical instruments, (including some of the best pianos in the world), snowmobiles, industrial engines, marine engines, lawnmowers, unmanned helicopters, Formula 1 racing car engines, industrial robots and even swimming pools!

Although Yamaha only started making motorcycles in the 1950s, its origins actually go back to the last century when Torakusu Yamaha started repairing organs in 1887. It was this that set Yamaha on a course that would eventually lead his company, Nippon Gakki, to become one of the world's foremost manufacturers of musical instruments. Before the turn of the century the company was not only a major supplier on the home market, but had already begun an export drive, which included shipping some 80 organs to Britain in 1892.

Although Torakusu Yamaha died in 1916 Nippon Gakki continued its expansion even when its production facilities were badly damaged by Allied bombing in 1945. They were able to slowly struggle back to resume making musical instruments by 1948.

During 1950 control of the company passed to Genichi Kawakami, then 38 years old. One of his first moves was to take the decision to begin motorcycle production even though the company had no previous experience. Their first model closely followed DKW's RT125 (as did BSA in Britain with the Bantam). From this came a long line of ever-improving 2-stroke models culminating with the RD Series in the 1970s and later the LC range. Running parallel was a policy of racing similar bikes.

Like Suzuki, Yamaha has largely switched production to 4-strokes, but even today the company still build a number of 2-strokes, albeit lightweights.

l. **1975 Yamaha TZ250 249cc,** water-cooled, twin cylinder, 2-stroke. **Est. £3,200–3,800** *BKS*

The mainstay of 250 and 350 class racing at national and international level for many years.

1984 Yamaha TR1 981cc, overhead camshaft V-twin, 75° aluminium cylinders and heads, twin Hitachi carburettors. **Est. £2,300–2,500** *BKS* *Japan's version of the vintage V-twin concept.*

l. **1983 Yamaha SRX 600 599cc,** single overhead camshaft twin port, triple disc brakes, chrome headlamp, square tube frame. **£1,300–1,500** *PC*

Modified after the classic café racer of the 1960s.

ZENITH *(British 1904–50)*

1921 Zenith Gradua 650cc, V-twin, complete and useable, excellent example of the marque. **£5,500–6,000** *BKS*

The Zenith became known best for its gearing, operated by expanding and contracting pulleys controlled by a side lever which gradually altered belt tension therefore giving rise to the 'Gradua' trade name.

RACING

Besides the great upsurge of interest in vintage and classic road bikes has come a parallel growth in the sporting side of older bikes; most notably racing. Today classic and vintage racing is an integral part of the world racing scene. In past days when a competition machine became outdated it was simply retired, but since the beginning of the 1980s this trend has been reversed, with many thousands of previously unwanted racers being put back into action. At first it was simply the original bikes being re-raced, often by their original riders, but with the high rises in values towards the end of the 1980s many bikes changed hands. Many too were exported, notably to Japan.

With the fall in prices during the early 1990s a new breed of classic racing appeared; bikes, and riders, new to the sport. It also saw the rise of the Forgotten Era class, the latter being open to bikes which were outlawed by classic rules (ie post-1968 2-strokes and post-1972 4-strokes). This let in many previously excluded machines such as the Yamaha TZ series and Suzuki RG500 four cylinder. For example, the famous Mallory Park post-TT meeting has races for both classic and Forgotten Era bikes; even the CRMC (Classic Racing Motorcycle Club) now allows Forgotten Era category bikes.

The post-TT meeting at Mallory brings mention of several ex-factory machines which had made appearances in the first few years. This list includes Mike Hailwood's 297cc Honda 6, various Benelli 4s, a 1939 AJS 500 water-cooled V-4, MV Agusta 350 and 500s, and even BMW and URS racing sidecar outfits from Germany.

When it comes to riders and sponsors the list is almost endless, even ex-world champions make appearances. This list of famous personalities is headed by none other than our Foreword writer this year, the great John Surtees, John being the only man to have won both bike and car world titles.

1950 Vincent-HRD Grey Flash 499cc, overhead valve. **£9,000–10,000** *PC*

The photograph shows John Surtees with the above machine which is very similar to the one with which he began his racing career.

The start of a 350cc Classic race at Cadwell Park. In the picture are Manx Nortons, AJS 7Rs, a Seeley and a Ducati.

1965 Aermacchi Ala d'Oro 248cc, overhead valve, early version of short-stroke 72 x 61mm engine, 5-speed gearbox, very good condition.
£6,000–7,000 *PC*

1952 AJS 7R 348cc, single overhead camshaft, 4-speed gearbox, dry clutch, conical brake hubs, swan neck clip-ons, immaculate condition.
£11,000–12,000 *PC*

l. **1950s BSA Gold Star DBD34 499cc,** full racing conversion including RRT2 gearbox, 2LS front brake, Dow forks, Amal GP carburettor, Lyta alloy tank, fly screen and racing megaphone exhaust.
£5,500–6,500 *PC*

1970 BSA Rocket 3 740cc, Rob North chassis, factory replica, triple disc brakes.
£5,000–5,500 *PC*

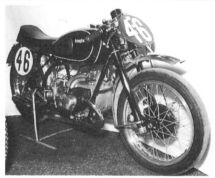

1950 Douglas Racer 500cc, special racing conversion, ridden by George Easton.
£2,500–3,000 *LDM*

1969 Ducati 350 Desmo Racer 348cc, 42mm Dell 'Orto carburettor, Oldani brakes, heavyweight forks.
£3,500–4,000 *PC*

This is a replica of Spaggiari's 1968/69 factory-machine, raced in Canada.

1957 Gilera 499cc, 4 cylinders, double overhead camshaft, original tyres, alloy dustbin fairing, leather saddle. Genuine ex-factory bike.
£200,000+ *PC*

1965 Greeves RCS Silverstone 246cc, very good condition.
£2,500–2,800 *GRA*

For a brief period in the mid-1960s the Greeves Silverstone was the dominant force in British 250cc category short circuit racing.

l. **1963 Honda CR93 124cc,** 6-speed gearbox, double-sided factory-type front brake.
£18,000–21,000 *PC*

1964 Honda CR110 49cc, double overhead camshaft, 8-speed gearbox, totally original.
£14,000–15,000   *PC*

1952 MV Agusta Bialbero 123.5cc Ex-Works Racing Model, twin overhead camshaft, 13bhp at 10,000rpm, centrally sprung forks, double-sided front brake drum.
£23,500–25,000   *S*

One of these machines took Cecil Sandford to MV's first world title, the 125cc, in 1952

1960 Norton Beart Manx 348cc, very good condition.
£15,000–18,000   *PC*

The actual Francis Beart machine ridden by Keith Heckles in the 1966 Manx Grand Prix.

1960s Norton Mularney Manx 499cc, 4-valve cylinder head developed by Leighton Buzzard engineer Syd Mularney.
£15,000+   *PC*

A unique machine, successfully raced in classic events by Bob Newby.

c1960 Marsh 498cc, 4 cylinder.
£20,000+   *PC*

Built by Southampton engineer Fred Marsh in his spare time. One man's answer to the mighty MV and Gilera.

1950s Norton Domiracer 646cc, race converted Dominator roadster.
£3,000–4,000   *PC*

1957/61 Norton Manx 348cc, completely renovated, excellent condition.
£12,000–12,500   *BKS*

1962 Norton 30M Manx 499cc.
£12,000–13,000   *PC*

Racing star of the 1960s, Dan Shorey, with a late model Ray Petty Manx during a Classic race meeting at Donington Park.

1971 Norton Norvil Production Racer 745cc,
overhead valve twin.
£4,000–5,000 *PC*

*Classic racer, Nick Sears, in race-winning form
at Cadwell Park.*

1972 Norton Petty Manx 499cc.
£18,000–20,000 *CRMC*

*Originally built by the late tuner, Ray Petty, from
new Manx spares, this machine has been ridden by
Derek Minter at CRMC events in 1995 and 1996.*

1960s Rickman Norton Twin 646cc, tuned
Norton twin cylinder engine, Rickman frame kit.
£4,000–5,000 *PC*

1948 Velocette KTT MkVIII 348cc, double overhead camshaft, original throughout.
£9,000–11,000 *Vel*

*Works versions won the first two 350cc class world
road racing championships in 1949 and 1950.*

SPECIALS & CAFE RACERS

The main strength of any Special motorcycle
is its individuality. The most popular Special
at present is the Triton, which uses a Triumph
engine fitted into a Norton Featherbed frame.

The first recorded Triton builder was
Londoner Doug 'Duki' Clarke. Working with
mechanic Ken Logman he put a twin
carburettor 650cc Triumph twin into an
ex-Manx Featherbed. Its first outing at
Silverstone was a success and the popularity
of this special has grown over the years.

Other early renowned Specials builders were
Monty and Ward who also produced their own
'bolt-on goodies'. Unity Equipe of Rochdale,
Lancashire, have been supplying parts to build
your own café racer for over thirty years and
are still very much in business. Ian Kennedy
produced many special machines in the late
'60s/early '70s, as did Paul Dunstall who

manufactured many of his own parts. But
surely, the most well-known Specials builder
would be Dave Degans of Dresda Auto's,
London, who has been successfully building
competitive Tritons since the early '60s.

There are so many variations of Specials,
such as Hybrids using superchargers or car
engines, triple cylindered 2-strokes
incorporating a 4th pot or Ernie Dorsett's
diesel-powered Matchless. This particular
motorbike uses a Robin generator motor and
returns 200mpg!

Specials are created using a selection of
parts from different machines. Whether for
off-road competition, green laning, street
performance or just sheer eccentricity,
Specials have always drawn the crowds.

John Newson – Oxney Motorcycles

1960s Triumph 649cc Sprinter,
AMC gearbox, Amal Monobloc
carburettor, BSA Bantam front fork
and brake, alloy wheel rims.
£700–800 *BKS*

1960 Velocette 348cc Special, overhead
camshaft single, unrestored condition.
Est. £3,200–3,500 *BKS*

*This machine was found in a London lock-up
garage and was believed to have lain there
unnoticed for some years, and is almost
entirely Velocette.*

1965 JAP Speedway 499cc, overhead valve, single cylinder, original condition, in running order.
Est. £1,100–1,600 *S*

1950 Moto Guzzi 500cc Special, leading link type front forks, alloy mudguards, good overall condition.
£1,200–1,500 *S*

1964 Norton Model 650SS 646cc Café Racer Conversion, good running condition.
Est. £2,000–2,800 *S*

Of all the sports twins of the 1960s, Norton's 650SS was the most natural for the café racer treatment, thanks to its race bred Featherbed frame. This machine has been fitted with an alloy petrol tank, sports seat, swept back exhaust pipes with Gold Star type silencers, rear sets and flat handlebars.

1967 Oxney Triumph 650cc Sprinter, overhead valve parallel twin, bore and stroke 71 x 82mm, methanol fuel, 2in SU carburettor, Shorrocks C75B supercharger, 3-speed AMC gearbox, AMC clutch, Triumph Tiger Cub front forks and wheel, Triumph rear wheel with 4in slick tyre, fuel and oil bearing frame.
£2,800–3,000 *OxM*

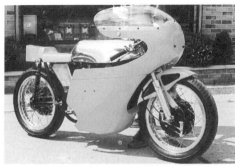

1970s Seely G50 Matchless AJS Racer APP 500cc, mechanics excellent, rebuilt to as new condition.
£12,000–13,000 *SW*

1958 Triton Wideline 850cc, Norton frame, Weslake sports engine.
£2,500–3,500 *AT*

1940/60s Pegasus Vincent 1459cc Drag Racing and Sprint Special, good condition.
£10,250–11,000 *BKS*

Built in the 1960s by Derek Chinn and Ian Messenger of Pegasus Engineering of Kempston Hardwick Bedfordshire. Power was provided by a Vincent V-twin engine running on methanol with lubrication by Castrol R. Both bore and stroke were enlarged to give 1459cc, Manx pistons of 90mm are fitted, and the bike has a single speed.

Raced at Santa Pod in the 1960s and '70s by Derek Chinn, Ian Messenger and a rider named Butler, it is said to have achieved 160mph for the standing quarter mile, no doubt aided by the Shorrocks CB72 supercharger and twin BTH racing magnetos on the timing chest.

r. **1975 Triumph Buccaneer 744cc,** overhead valve engine, custom built bodywork, triple Lockheed racing disc brakes, alloy rims, single seat.
£4,500–5,000 *TOC*

SIDECARS

1927 AJS 350cc & Coachbuilt Sidecar,
very good condition.
£4,000–5,000 *VER*

**1914 BSA Model K 557cc Combination,
with BSA Model No. 2 Sidecar,** only
3 owners from new, 600 miles, engine changed,
excellent running order.
£8,000–9,000 *BKS*

**1955 BSA 650 A10 Gold Flash 646cc, with
Busmar Double Adult Sidecar,** overhead
valve twin cylinder, 4-speed gearbox, very
good condition.
£2,300–2,500 *PM*

*The double adult sidecar and A10 Gold
Flash were a popular means of family
transport in 1955. Today they are a rare
sight on Britain's roads.*

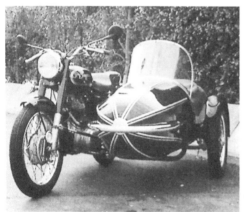

**1992 Enfield India 500cc Motorcycle
Combination,** only 900 miles,
very good condition.
£2,000–3,000 *ADT*

**1957 Ariel Square Four 4G MkII 995cc with
Watsonian GP Sidecar,** completely restored,
brown and black livery, very good condition.
£5,200–6,000 *BKS*

**1921 BSA 986cc Motorcycle & Taxi
Combination,** V-twin side valve engine, very
good condition.
£20,000+ *VMCC*

*There are only 2 of this model in the world. This
particular bike is the original show model that
was used by BSA and is also the bike pictured in
the brochures and parts books.*

**1962 BSA A10 647cc, with Watsonian Sports
Sidecar,** later twin lead front brake, good condition.
£2,800–3,000 *BLM*

*The tank cover and twin leading shoe front brake
are non-standard.*

**1925 FN M50 750cc, with Mills Fulford Sidecar
Combination,** very good condition.
£11,500–12,500 *BKS*

*The Belgian FN factory was famous for production of
their in-line 4 cylinder motorcycles. Up until 1924 they
firmly adopted shaft drive to the rear wheel but changed
to chain drive in 1925. The new chain drive model for
1925 was designated the M50 and adopted an overhead
inlet and side valve exhaust 52 x 88mm 748cc engine
specification. The engine unit was impressive with a
large car type crank case with clutch and gearbox bolted
to the rear.*

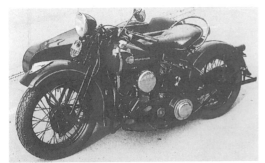

**1938 Harley-Davidson 'Flathead' 1200cc
with Sidecar,** side valve flathead, 74cu in,
good condition.
£12,500–13,500 *C*

**1937 Indian Chief 80cu in Motorcycle and
Sidecar,** fitted with 1952 side valve V-twin engine,
3-speed gearbox, later telescopic forks, good
condition throughout.
Est. £8,000–10,000 *S*

**1950 Panther 600cc Combination with Swallow
Sidecar,** fully restored to as new condition by
Tennant-Eyles.
£7,000–8,000 *BKS*

*In single family ownership for some years, this
combination was still being ridden regularly on the
Isle of Man until 1989.*

1913 Rudge Multi 3½hp 499cc Combination,
fully restored to concours condition.
£25,000+ *REC*

r. **1925 Triumph SD 550cc Combination
with Gloria Sidecar,** gas lighting, original
and unrestored.
£4,500–5,500 *HCH*

**1964 Honda CZ100 49cc Monkey Bike &
Sidecar,** overhead valve, very good condition.
£1,650–1,850 *MAY*

**1959 Matchless CSR Twin Sprint 646cc
Motorcycle Combination,** overhead valve,
very good condition.
£4,500–5,000 *PC*

Excellent competition history.

1937 Royal Enfield KX 1140cc Combination,
V-twin, fully restored.
£6,500–8,000 *AT*

**1936 Scott Cyc-auto 98cc Autocycle
Combination with Watsonian Child's Sidecar,**
2-stroke mounted transversely below the front down
tube, drive through worm gear to a chain driving the
rear wheel, good original condition, would benefit
from a sympathetic restoration.
£750–900 *BKS*

1929 Triumph CSD 549cc Combination, single cylinder, side valve, non-standard exhaust system and magneto, otherwise correct, good condition, acetylene lights.
£2,000–3,000 *PS*

1955 Triumph Tiger 110 649cc Combination with Garrard GP Sports Sidecar, magneto needs attention, otherwise good mechanical condition, many original fittings such as Avon Streamliner dustbin fairing, chrome luggage racks, 'D' rear crash bars and alpine twin horns, the sidecar has a double duck hood, spotlight, front crash bar, braked wheel and detachable mountings.
£4,200–4,500 *BKS*

1970 Triumph Trophy 649cc Combination with Watsonian Sidecar, good condition.
£2,800–3,100 *AT*

1977 Honda Gold Wing Executive GL1000 Motorcycle Combination.
£5,000–6,000 *CCR*
One of only 50 produced.

MOPEDS

1969 Ariel 3 49cc.
£200–250 *MAY*
Dutch Anker-engined BSA group sales flop.

1955 De Dion Moped 49cc, in running order.
£600–650 *DB*

l. **1966 Mobylette 49cc Moped.**
£40–50 *PS*

1979 Garelli Katia 49cc Moped, pivoted fork rear suspension, front mudguard missing.
£40–50 *PS*
The Italian Garelli range was imported by Agrati Sales of Nottingham.

r. **1959 Norman Nippy 49cc.**
£200–270 *MAY*

1958 NSU Quickly L 49cc.
£200–270 *MAY*

De luxe version of the best-selling Quickly moped. Differences include partial enclosure of rear wheel, leg shields, and other minor improvements.

1968 Raleigh Runabout 49cc Moped, single cylinder, 2-stroke, complete, with spare engine, requires restoration.
£50–60 *PS*

SCOOTERS

1961 BSA Sunbeam 249cc, twin cylinder, overhead valve, Lucas reconditioned electric starter, spare wheel and carrier.
£320–400 *PS*

Restored example of the BSA group's Sunbeam scooter. Also sold as the Triumph Tigress 249cc overhead valve twin cylinder engine.

1947 Corgi Runabout 98cc, 2-stroke, single cylinder, restored.
£300–400 *PS*

1958 Lambretta LDB 150 147cc.
£800–850 *MAY*

1957 Lambretta 150LD 150cc, original concours condition.
£2,000–2,500 *CRC*

r. **1957 Maico Modil 197cc,** large wheel, comprehensive weather protection.
£1,500–2,000 *MOC*

1962 Lambretta LI 150 Series 3 147cc, styled by Bertone, 2-stroke, original single seats, chrome accessories including carrier, side panel guards, front mudguard trim.
£2,800–3,200 *C*

1956 NSU Prima 146cc.
£350–450 *MAY*

1956 Piatti 124cc, rare, restored.
£400–500 *PS*

Manufactured under licence by Cyclemaster, Byfleet, Surrey.

1963 Raleigh Roma 71.5cc, horizontal 2-stroke, 3-speed gearbox, restored to original specification.
£200–300 *PS*

Licence built version of the Italian Bianchi Bi Bi.

l. **1957 TWN Contessa 197cc,** 2-stroke, fan-cooled, 12 volt electrics, good overall condition.
£600–800 *S*

1955 Vespa GS 150 USI 149cc.
£2,000–2,500 *MAY*

Very rare model.

l. **1957 Vespa 42 L2 149cc.**
£650–750 *MAY*

MINI MOTORCYCLES

l. **1974 Harley-Davidson X90 89cc,** 2-stroke, 4-speeds.
£800–1,000 *PC*

One of the most prized of all mini-bikes, the X90 was made at the Italian division of Harley-Davidson in Varese, now home to Cagiva.

1973 Honda CF70 Chaly 71.8cc, overhead camshaft, single cylinder, 3-speed gearbox, original condition.
£300–400 *S*

l. **1974 Honda ST70 • 71.8cc,** overhead camshaft, high level exhaust, split rims, fold-down handlebars.
£400–500 *PC*

RESTORATION PROJECTS

1921 Allon 275cc, Villiers 2-stroke, single-speed belt drive transmission, missing front wheel, substantially complete and original, restoration project.
£1,200–1,400　*BKS*

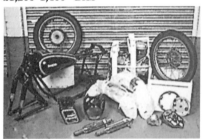

1956 Douglas Dragonfly 350cc, purchased for restoration several years ago, tank, cycle parts and all ironwork refurbished, most chromework completed, new silencers and tyres, rebuilt wheels, together with a spare parts book and maintenance manual.
£1,200–1,400　*BKS*

1964 Honda C110 49cc, overhead camshaft, in need of restoration.
£80–100　*MAY*

1937 Rudge Ulster 500cc, restoration project.
£1,000–1,300　*CStC*

c1955 BSA B31 348cc, swinging-arm frame, substantially complete, restoration project.
£350–450　*BKS*

l. **1955 Ducati Cucciolo 48cc.**
Est. £600–1,000
BKS

1954 Gilera 150 149cc, overhead valve, restoration project.
£320–480　*MAY*

1920 Rover 3½hp Solo, single cylinder, side valve, 3-speed Sturmey Archer gearbox, belt drive to rear wheel, leather pan seat, aluminium footboards, rear carrier, leather-fronted tool boxes, relatively complete, a satisfying restoration project.
Est. £2,750–3,000　*BKS*

1919 Triumph Junior 225cc, 2-stroke, single cylinder, complete apart from some missing handlebar controls, dry stored for decades, requires restoration.
£1,000–1,200　*PS*

l. **c1976 Volkswagen/Cossack 1250cc Special,** air-cooled, 4-cylinder Volkswagen engine driving what appears to be a Russian Cossack gearbox, Japanese forks, modified Cossack frame, substantially complete, in reasonable condition, interesting restoration project at minimal cost.
£180–250　*S*

Signs & Pumps

An ROP Zip Super Spirit Motor Oil Enamel Sign, some chipping to front, 43 x 85in (110 x 216cm).
Est. £220–280 *BKS*

A Pre-War Shell Petrol Pump Globe.
£250–300 *GAZ*

A 1950s Illuminated BSA Sign, 8¼ x 14¼in (21 x 36cm).
£100–150 *CRC*

A 1950s Plastic Michelin Man Sign.
£40–50 *GAZ*

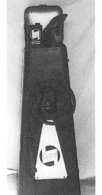

A 1950s Castrol Oil Dispenser, by John B Pillin Ltd.
£100–200 *CRC*

A 1930s Silkolene Oils Enamel Sign, excellent condition, 15 x 30in (38 x 76cm).
£120–130 *SW*

l. **A 1930s Desmo St Christopher Mascot.**
£60–70 *ATF*

A 1960s 5 Gallon Millers Oils Can, 20in (51cm) high.
£10–15 *CRC*

A mid-1950s RAC Repairer Enamel Sign, good condition, 57 x 65in (145 x 165cm).
£100–110 *SW*

A 1950s Castrol Pressure Grease Pump, 28in (71cm) high.
£50–100 *CRC*

An Air and Water Dispenser, by PCL Sheffield, 66½in (169cm) high.
£75–125 *CRC*

A c1955 Illuminated Sales Sign, 36½in (93cm) high.
£50–150 *CRC*

Manuals & Brochures

Greeves The Choice of the Expert, 1962 brochure, 7 x 9in (17.5 x 23cm).
£10–15 *DM*

Three *Sunbeam Motorcycles,* manuals, 1928 and 1940s.
£30–40 *MR*

A Selection of Motorcycle Manuals.
£12–22 each *MR*

l. **James Motorcycles 1936** brochure, 7 x 10in (17.5 x 25cm).
£20–25 *DM*

Triumph Hints & Tips for Motorcyclists, 1913, 6 x 4½in (15 x 11.5cm).
£30–35 *DM*

l. **Royal Enfield Motorcycles 1957** brochure, 8 x 9½in (20.5 x 24cm).
£15–20 *DM*

Grindlay Peerless Motorcycles and Sidecars 1927 brochure, 10 x 6½in (25.5 x 16.5cm).
£10–12 *DM*

Francis-Barnett 1959 brochure, 9½ x 7in (24 x 17.5cm).
£10–14 *DM*

Motorcycle Art

Mike Hailwood, by Jim Blanchard
Gouache, 14¼ x 18½in (36 x 47cm).
£24–30 *JIB*

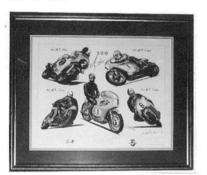

Ago – The M.V. Years, by Jim Blanchard Gouache, limited edition print, 1 of 5, 14¼ x 18½in (36 x 47cm) framed and glazed.
£24–30 *JIB*

A Dollar Motorcycles Full-Colour Lithograph Poster, linen-backed, unframed, c1930, 66 x 48in (168 x122cm).
£3,750–4,000 *BKS*

Two Auto & Moto Club de France 4-Colour Lithograph Posters, linen-backed, unframed, dated '6–'35', 15 x 12in (38 x 31cm).
£280–320 *BKS*

r. **Honda Works Riders of the '60s, by Jim Blanchard** Gouache, 14¼ x 18½in (36 x 47cm).
£24–30 *JIB*

l. **Tigers, by Roy Barrett** Watercolour, 14 x 17in (35.5 x 43cm).
£300–400 *ROY*

l. **An Ashford Grass Speedway Poster,** printed in red and blue, 30 x 20in (76 x 51cm).
Est. £240–300 *S*

Joey's Island, by Rod Organ Oil on canvas, signed by Joey on the back, 20 x 30in (51 x 76cm).
£1,000–1,300 *ROD*

Joey Dunlop, MBE OBE, the most successful TT rider of all time, approaches the gooseneck on his Honda RC45 750 on his way to his 19th TT win and to 1995 Senior TT.

Two Colour Lithograph Posters,
l. Manurhin Scooters, c1958.
r. Jaguar Bernardet Scooters, c1958.
Est. £80–120 *BKS*

A BSA Full-Colour Lithograph Poster, linen-backed, for French Concessionaires, unframed, 22 x 16in (56 x 40cm), together with a contemporary Christmas card and printed mailing envelope, unused condition.
£200–250 *BKS*

GLOSSARY

We have attempted to define some of the terms that you will come across in this book. If there are any other terms or technicalities you would like explained or you feel should be included in future editions, please let us know.

ACU – Auto Cycle Union, who control a large part of British motorcycle sport.

Advanced ignition – Ignition timing set causing firing before the piston reaches centre top, variation is now automatic.

Air-cooling – Most motorcycles rely on air-cooling to the atmosphere.

Air intake – The carburettor port admitting air to mix with fuel from the float chamber.

AMCA – Amateur Motor Cycle Association, promoters of English off-road events.

APMC – The Association of Pioneer Motor Cyclists.

Auto Cycle Club – Formed in 1903 it was the original governing body of motorcycle sport, in 1907 became the Auto Cycle Union.

Automatic inlet valve – Activated by the engine suction. Forerunner of the mechanically operated valve.

Balloon tyres – Wide section, low pressure, soft running tyres, used on tourers for comfort.

Beaded-edge tyres – Encased rubber beads in channel on wheel rim.

Belt drive – A leather or fabric belt from engine or gearbox to rear wheel.

BHP – A measure of engine output, e.g. to lift 33,000lb one foot in a minute requires one horsepower.

BMCRC – British Motor Cycle Racing Club, formed in 1909.

BMF – British Motorcycle Federation.

Bore/stroke ratio – Cylinder diameter ratio to stroke.

Cam – Device for opening and closing a valve.

Camshaft – The mounting shaft for the cam, can be in low, high or overhead position.

Carburettor – Used to produce the air/fuel mixture.

Chain drive – Primary form of drive from engine to gearbox and secondary gearbox to rear wheel.

Combustion chamber – Area where the fuel/air mixture is compressed and fired, between piston and cylinder head.

Compression ratio – The fuel/air mixture compression degree.

Crankcase – The casing enclosing the crankshaft and its attachments.

Crankshaft – The shaft for converting the up–and down piston motion into rotary.

Cylinder – Containing the piston and capped by the cylinder head, is the site of the explosion which provides power.

Cylinder head – In a vertical engine caps off the top end of the cylinder. In a 4–stroke engine carries the valves.

Damper – Used for slowing down movement in suspension system or as crankshaft balance.

Displacement – The engine capacity or amount of volume displaced by the movement of the piston from bottom dead centre to top dead centre.

Distributor – A gear driven contact sending high tension current to spark plugs.

DOHC – Double overhead camshaft.

Dry sump – Two oil pumps, one supplying oil to the bearings from a tank, the other to return it to the tank.

Earles forks – An unusual front fork design. A long leading link and rigid pivot through both links behind the wheel.

Featherbed – A Norton frame, designed by Rex and Crommie McCandless, Belfast, used for racing machines from 1950, road machines from 1953.

FIM – Federation Internationale Motorcycliste, controls motorcycle sport worldwide.

Flat head – A flat surfaced cylinder head.

Flat twin – An engine with 2 horizontally opposed cylinders, or 4 to make a Flat Four.

Float – A plastic or brass box which floats upon the fuel in a float chamber and operates the needle valve controlling the fuel.

Flywheel – Attached to the crankshaft this heavy wheel smooths intermittent firing impulses and helps slow running.

Friction drive – An early form of drive using discs in contact instead of chains and gears.

Gearbox – Cased trains of pinion wheels which can be moved to provide alternative ratios.

Gear ratios – Differential rates of speed between sets of pinions to provide higher or lower rotation of the rear wheel in relation to the engine.

GP – Grand Prix, an international race to a fixed formula.

High camshaft – Mounted high up on the engine to shorten the pushrods in an ohv formation.

IOE – Inlet over exhaust, a common arrangement with an overhead inlet and side exhaust.

Leaf spring – Metal blades clamped and bolted together, used in suspension many years ago.

Magneto – A high tension dynamo producing current for the ignition spark. Superseded by coil ignition.

Main bearings – Bearings in which the crankshaft runs.

Manifold – Collection of pipes supplying mixture or taking away fumes.

MCC – The Motor Cycling club which runs sporting events. Formed in 1902.

Moped – A light motorcycle of under 50cc with pedals attached.

OHC – Overhead camshaft, can be either single or double.

OHV – Overhead valve engine.

Overhead cam – An engine with overhead camshaft or camshafts operating its valves.

Overhead valve – A valve mounted in the cylinder head.

Pinking – A distinctive noise from an engine with over-advanced ignition or inferior fuel.

Piston – The component driven down the cylinder by expanding gases.

Post-vintage – A motorcycle made after December 31, 1930 and before January 1, 1945.

Pressure plate – The plate against which the clutch springs react to load the friction plates.

Pushrods – Operating rods for overhead valves, working from cams below the cylinder.

Rotary valve – A valve driven from the camshaft for inlet or exhaust and usually a disc or cylinder shape. For either 2-or 4-stroke engines.

SACU – Scottish Auto Cycle Union, which controls motorcycle sport in Scotland.

SAE – Society of Automotive Engineers. Used in a system of classifying engine oils such as SAE30, IOW/50 etc.

Shock absorber – A damper, used to control up-and-down movement of suspension or to cushion a drive train.

Silencer – Device fitted to the exhaust system of an engine whereby the pressure of the exhaust gases is considerably reduced before reaching the outer air.

Swinging arm – Rear suspension by radius arms carrying the wheel and attached to the frame at the other end.

Torque – Twisting rotational force in a shaft, can be measured to show at what point an engine develops most torque.

INDEX TO ADVERTISERS

BIBLIOGRAPHY

Bacon, Roy; British Motorcycles of the 1930s, Osprey, 1986.
Bacon, Roy; Matchless & AJS Restoration, Osprey, 1993.
Bacon, Roy; Norton Twin Restoration, Osprey, 1993.
Bacon Roy; Triumph Twins & Triples, Osprey, 1990.
Birkitt Malcolm; Harley-Davidson, Osprey, 1993.
Champ, Robert Cordon; Sunbeam S7/S8 Super Profile, Haynes, 1983.
Davis, Ivor; It's a Triumph, Haynes, 1980.
Morley Don; and Woolett, Mick; Classic Motorcycles, BMW, Osprey, 1992.
Morley, Don; Classic Motorcycles, Triumph, Osprey, 1991.
Stuart, Garry; and Carroll, John; Classic Motorcycles, Indian, Osprey, 1994.
Tragatsch, Erwin, ed; The New Illustrated Encyclopedia of Motorcycles, Grange Books, 1993

Walker, Mick; Classic Motorcycles, Honda, Osprey, 1993.
Walker, Mick; Classic European Racing Motorcycles, Osprey, 1992.
Walker, Mick; Classic Italian Racing Motorcycles, Osprey, 1991.
Walker, Mick; Classic Japanese Racing Motorcycles, Osprey, 1991.
Walker, Mick; Classic Motorcycles, Ducati, Osprey, 1993.
Walker, Mick; Classic Motorcycles, Kawasaki, Osprey, 1993.
Walker, Mick; Classic Motorcycles, Suzuki, Osprey, 1993.
Walker, Mick; Classic Motorcycles, Yamaha, Osprey, 1993.
Wherrett, Duncan; Classic Motorcycles, Vincent, Osprey, 1994.
Woollett, Mick; Norton, Osprey, 1992.

DIRECTORY OF MOTORCYCLE CLUBS

If you wish to be included in next year's directory or if you have a change of address or telephone number, please could you inform us by 30th April 1997. Entries will be repeated in subsequent editions unless we are requested otherwise.

ABC Owners Club, D. S. Hales, The Hedgerows, Sutton St Nicholas, Hereford & Worcester, HR1 3BU Tel: 01432 880726

AJS & Matchless Owners Club, 25 Victoria Street, Irthlingborough, Northamptonshire, NN9 5RG Tel: 01933 652155

AMC Owners Club, c/o Terry Corley, 12 Chilworth Gardens, Sutton, Surrey, SM1 3SP

Androd Classics, 70 Broadway, Frome, Somerset, BA11 3HE Tel: 01373 471087

Ariel Owners Motor Cycle Club, Swindon Branch, 45 Wheeler Avenue, Swindon, Wiltshire, SN2 6HQ

Ariel Owners Motor Cycle Club, Andy Hemingway, 80 Pasture Lane, Clayton, Bradford, Yorkshire, BD14 6LN

Bantam Enthusiasts Club, c/o Vic Salmon, 16 Oakhurst Close, Walderslade, Chatham, Kent, ME5 9AN

Benelli Owners Club, c/o Rosie Marston, 14 Rufford Close, Barton Seagrave, Kettering, Northamptonshire, NN15 6RF

BMW Club, c/o John Lawes (Vintage Secretary), Bowbury House, Kirk Langley, Ashbourne, Derbyshire, DE6 4NJ Tel: 01332 824334

BMW Owners Club, c/o Mike Cox, 22 Combermere, Thornbury, Bristol, Avon, BS12 2ET
Tel & Fax: 01454 415358

Bristol & Avon Roadrunners Motorcycle Club, 177 Speedwell Road, Speedwell, Bristol, Avon, BS5 7SP

Bristol & District Sidecar Club, 158 Fairlyn Drive, Kingswood, Bristol, Avon, BS15 4PZ

Bristol Genesis Motorcycle Club, Burrington, 1a Bampton Close, Headley Park, Bristol, Avon, BS13 7QZ. Tel: 0117 978 2584

British Motor Bike Owners Club, c/o Ray Peacock, Crown Inn, Shelfanger, Diss, Norfolk, IP22 2DL

British Motorcycle Owners Club, c/o Phil Coventry, 59 Mackenzie Street, Bolton, Lancashire, BL1 6QP

British Motorcyclists Federation, 129 Seaforth Avenue, Motspur Park, New Malden, Surrey, KT3 6JU

British Two Stroke Owners Club, c/o Mark Hathaway, 45 Moores Hill, Olney, Buckinghamshire, MK46 5DY

Brough Superior Club, c/o Piers Otley, 6 Canning Road, Felpham, Sussex, PO22 7AD

BSA Owners Club, 44 Froxfield Road, West Leigh, Havant, Hampshire, PO9 5PW

CBX Riders Club, c/o Peter Broad, 57 Osborne Close, Basingstoke, Hampshire, RG21 2TS

Chiltern Vehicle Preservation Group, Chiltern House, Aylesbury, Buckinghamshire, HP17 8BY Tel: 01296 651283

Christian Motorcycle Association North, c/o Mr A. Sutton, 100 Low Bank Road, Ashton-in-Makerfield, Wigan, Greater Manchester, WN4 9RZ

Classic Racing Motorcycle Club, Membership Secretary, 33 Healey Avenue, High Wycombe, Buckinghamshire, HP13 7JP

Cossack Owners Club, c/o Mr Charles Hancock, Lake View, Carr Road, North Kelsey, Lincolnshire, LN7 6LB

Cotton Owners & Enthusiasts Club, c/o Peter Turner, 'Coombehayes', Sidmouth Road, Lyme Regis, Dorset, DT7 3EQ

DKW Rotary Owners Club, c/o David Cameron, Dunbar, Ingatestone Road, Highwood, Chelmsford, Essex, CM1 3QU

Dot Owners Club, c/o Chris Black, 115 Lincoln Avenue, Clayton, Newcastle-upon-Tyne, Tyne & Wear, ST5 3AR

Ducati Owners Club, 131 Desmond Drive, Old Catton, Norwich, Norfolk, NR6 7JR

Francis Barnett Owners Club, 58 Knowle Road, Totterdown, Bristol, Avon, BS4 2ED

Gold Star Owners Club, c/o George Chiswell, 43 Church Lane, Kitts Green, Birmingham, West Midlands, B33 9EG

Goldwing Owners Club, 82 Farley Close, Little Stoke, Bristol, Avon, BS12 6HG

Greeves Owners Club, c/o Dave McGregor, 4 Longshaw Close, North Wingfield, Chesterfield, Derbyshire, S42 5QR

Greeves Riders Association, Dave & Brenda McGregor, 4 Longshaw Close, North Wingfield, Chesterfield, Staffordshire, S42 5QR Tel: 01246 853846

Harley Davidson Owners Club, 1 St Johns Road, Clifton, Bristol, Avon, BS8 2ET

Harley Davidson Riders Club of Great Britain, SAE to Membership Secretary PO Box 62, Newton Abbott, Devon, TQ12 2QE

Hesketh Owners Club, c/o Tom Wilson, 19 Stonnall Road, Aldridge, Walsall, West Midlands, W59 8JX

Historic Raleigh Motorcycle Club, c/o R. Thomas, 22 Valley Road, Solihull, West Midlands, B92 9AD

Honda Owners Club (GB), c/o Dave Barton, 18 Embley Close, Calmore, Southampton, Hampshire, SO40 2QX

Indian Motorcycle Club, c/o John Chatterton (Membership Secretary), 183 Buxton Road, Newtown, New Mills, Stockport, Cheshire, SK12 3LA Tel: 01663 747106

International CBX Owners Association, 24 Pevensey Way, Paddock Hill, Frimley, Camberley, Surrey, GU16 5YJ Tel: 01252 836698

International Laverda Owners Club, c/o Alan Cudipp, Orchard Cottage, Orchard Terrace, Acomb, Hexham, Northumberland, NE46 4QB

Italian Motorcycle Owners Club, c/o Rosie Marston (Membership Secretary), 14 Rufford Close, Barton Seagrove, Kettering, Northamptonshire, NN15 6RF

Jawa-CZ Owners Club, John Blackburn 39 Bignor Road, Sheffield, Yorkshire, S6 IJD

Kawasaki Owners Club, c/o John Dalton, 37 Hinton Road, Runcorn, Cheshire, WA7 5PZ

LE Velo Club Ltd, Kevin Parsons, Chapel Mead, Blandford Hill, Winterbourne, Whitechurch, Blandford, Dorset, DT11 0AB

Laverda Owners Club, c/o Ray Sheepwash, 8 Maple Close, Swanley, Kent, BR8 7YN

London Douglas Motorcycle Club,
c/o Reg Holmes (Membership Secretary),
48 Standish Avenue, Stoke Lodge, Patchway,
Bristol, Avon, BS12 6AG
Maico Owners Club, c/o Phil Hingston,
'No Elms', Goosey, Faringdon, Oxfordshire,
SN7 8PA Tel: 01367 710408
Military Vehicle Trust, PO Box 6, Fleet,
Hampshire, GU13 9PE
Morini Owners Club, c/o Richard Laughton,
20 Fairford Close, Church Hill, Redditch,
Hereford & Worcester, B98 9LU
Morini Riders Club, c/o Kevin Bennett,
1 Glebe Farm Cottages, Sutton Veney, Warminster,
Wiltshire, BA12 7AS
Moto Guzzi Club GB, c/o Jenny Trengove,
53 Torbay Road, Harrow,
Middlesex, HA2 9QQ
MV Agusta Club GB, c/o Martyn Simpkins,
31 Baker Street, Stapenhill,
Burton-on-Trent, Staffordshire, DE15 9AF
MV Agusta Owners Club,
c/o Ray Gascoine, 7 Lowes Lane, Wellisbourne,
Nr Warwick, Staffordshire, CV35 9RB
MZ Riders Club (South West), c/o Alex Pearce,
80 Kingskirswell Road, Newton Abbott,
Devon, TQ12 1DG.
Tel: 01626 331584
National Autocycle & Cyclemotor Club,
c/o Rob Harknett, 1 Parkfields, Roydon, Harlow,
Essex, CM19 5JA
National Hill Climb Association,
43 Tyler Close, Hanham, Bristol, Avon, BS15 3RG
Tel: 0117 944 3569
New Imperial Owners Association,
c/o Mike Slater, 3 Fairview Drive, Higham,
Kent, ME3 7BG

North Devon British Motorcycle Owners Club,
c/o Mrs Y Coleman,
Bassett Lodge, Pollards Hill,
Little Torrington, Devon, EX38 8JA
Norton Owners Club, c/o Dave Fenner, Beeches,
Durley Brook Road, Durley, Southhampton,
Hampshire, SO32 2AR
Panther Owners Club, c/o A. & J. Jones, Coopers
Cottage, Park Lane, Castle Camps, Cambridge,
Cambridgeshire, CB1 6SR
Riders for Health, The Old Vicarage, Norton,
Daventry, Northamptonshire,
NN11 5ND
Royal Enfield Owners Club,
c/o John Cherry, Meadow Lodge Farm, Henfield,
Coalpit Heath, Avon, BS17 2UX
Rudge Enthusiasts Club, c/o Colin Kirkwood,
41 Rectory Green, Beckenham, Kent, BR3 4HX
Tel: 0181 658 0494
Scott Owners Club, c/o H. Beal, 2 Whiteshott,
Basildon, Essex, SS16 5HF
Shrivenham Motorcycle Club,
12-14 Townsend Road, Shrivenham, Swindon,
Wiltshire, SN6 8AS
Sidecar Register, c/o John Proctor,
112 Briarlyn Road, Birchencliffe, Huddersfield,
Yorkshire, HD3 3NW
**Street Specials Motorcycle Club inc Rickman
O/C, Harris O/C and Featherbed O/C,**
c/o Dominic Dawson, 12 St Mark's Close, Gosport,
Hampshire, PO12 2DB
Tel: 01705 501321
Sunbeam Owners Club,
c/o Stewart Engineering, Church Terrace, Harbury,
Leamington Spa,
Warwickshire, CV33 9HL
Sunbeam Owners Fellowship, PO Box 7,
Market Harborough, Leicestershire.
Suzuki Owners Club, Membership,
Mark Fitz-Gibbon, 3 Rossetti Lodge, Burns Road,
Royston, Hertfordshire, SG8 5SF
Trident and Rocket Three Owners Club,
63 Dunbar Road, Southport, Merseyside, PR8 4RJ
Triumph Motorcycle Club,
6 Hortham Lane, Almondsbury, Bristol,
Avon, BS12 4JH
Triumph Owners Club, c/o Mrs M. Mellish,
4 Douglas Avenue, Harold Wood, Romford,
Essex, RM3 0UT
Velocette Owners Club, c/o David Allcock,
3 Beverley Drive, Trinity Fields, Stafford,
Staffordshire, ST16 1RR
Velocette Owners Club, c/o Vic Blackman,
1 Mayfair, Tilehurst, Reading, Berks, RG30 4RA
Vespa Club of Great Britain, Membership
Secretary, Mr S. Barbour, 254 Braehead, Bonhill,
Alexandria, Dunbartonshire, Scotland, G83 9NE
Vincent Owners Club, c/o Andy Davenport,
Ashley Cottage, 133 Bath Road, Atworth, Wiltshire,
SN12 8LA
Vintage Japanese Motorcycle Club,
9 Somerset Crescent, Melksham, Wiltshire,
SN12 7LX Tel: 01225 702816
Vintage Motor Cycle Club, Allen House,
Wetmore Road, Burton-on-Trent, Staffordshire,
DE14 1TR Tel: 01283 540557
Vintage Motor Scooter Club,
c/o Ian Harrop, 11 Ivanhoe Avenue, Lowton
St Lukes, Nr Warrington, Cheshire, WA3 2HX
Vintage Motorcycle Club of Ulster,
c/o Mrs M. Burns, 20 Coach Road, Comber,
Newtownards, Co Down, Ireland, BT23 5QX
ZI Owners Club, c/o Sam Holt, 54 Hawthorne
Close, Congleton, Cheshire, CW12 4UF

DIRECTORY OF MUSEUMS

Battlesbridge Motorcycle Museum
Muggeridge Farm, Maltings Road, Battlesbridge,
SS11 7RF
Tel: 01268 769392/560866
An interesting collection of classic motorcycles &
scooters in a small informal museum. Open Suns
10.30am-4pm. Adults £1, children free.

Birmingham Museum of Science & Industry
136 Newhall Street, Birmingham, B3 1RZ
Tel: 0121 235 1651
A small collection of motorcycles. Open Mon to Sat
9.30am-5pm. Sun 2pm-5pm. Closed December 25-26,
and January 1. Admission free.

Bristol Industrial Museum
Princes Wharf, City Docks, Bristol, BS1 4RN
Tel: 0117 925 1470
A small collection of Bristol-made Douglas machines,
including the only surviving V4 of 1908, and a 1972
Quasar. Open Saturday to Wednesday 10am-1pm
and 2pm-5pm. Closed Thurs and Fri, also Good
Friday, December 25-27 and January 1. Adults £2,
under 16s free.

Brooklands Museum
The Clubhouse, Brooklands Road, Weybridge,
KT13 0QN Tel: 01932 857381
The birthplace of British motorsport and aviation,
Brooklands has several motorcycles on display. Open
Saturday and Sunday 10am-4pm. Guided tours at
10.30am and 2pm on Tues, Weds and Thurs. Adults
£4, OAPs & students £3, children £2.

Cotton's Classic Bikes, Phil
Victoria Road Museum, Ulverston, LA12 0BY
Tel: 01229 586099
Working museum, most exhibits are available to buy.
Open 10am-4.30pm Tues-Sat, closed Sun & Mon.

Craven Collection of Classic Motorcycles
Brockfield Villa, Stockton-on-the-Forest, YO3 9UE
Tel: 01904 488461/400493
Private collection of over 180 Vintage & Post-War
Classic Motorcycles. Open to the public on first
Sunday of every month and Bank Holiday Mondays,
10am-4pm. Club visits & private parties arranged.
Adults £2.50, Children under 10 Free.

Foulkes-Halbard of Filching
Filching Manor, Jevington Road, Wannock,
Polegate, BN26 5QA Tel: 01323 487838
30 motorcycles, including pre-'40s American bikes
ex-Steve McQueen, 100 cars, 1893-1993. Open 7 days a
week in summer 10.30-4.30pm. Thurs-Sun in winter,
or by appt. Adults £3, OAPs and children £2.

Grampian Transport Museum
Main Street, Alford, Aberdeenshire, AB33 8AD
Tel: 019755 62292
30-40 machines ranging from a 1902 Beeston
Humber to a Norton F1. Mods and Rockers caff
display with Triton and Triumph Tina scooter.
Competition section with 1913 Indian twin and 1976
Rob North replica Trident racer. Open March 28-
October 31, 10am-5pm. Adults £2.30, children 80p,
OAPs £1.50, family ticket £5.

Haynes Sparkford Motor Museum
Sparkford, Yeovil, BA22 7LH Tel: 01963 440804
30 plus machines from 1914 BSA onwards. Video
theatre. Bookshop. Open Mon-Sun 9.30am-5.30pm.
Closed December 25-26 and January 1. Adults £4.50,
OAPs £4, children £2.75.

Murray's Motorcycle Museum
Bungalow Corner, TT Course, Isle of Man.
Tel: 01624 861719
140 machines, with Hailwood's 250cc Mondial and
Honda 125cc and the amazing 500cc 4 cylinder
roadster designed by John Wooler. Open May-Sept
10am-5pm. Adults £2, OAPs & children £1.

Museum of British Road Transport
St. Agnes Lane, Hales Street, Coventry, CV1 1PN
Tel: 01203 832425

65 motorcycles, from local firms such as Coventry
Eagle, Coventry Victor, Francis-Barnett, Triumph
and Rudge. Close to city centre. Open every day
except December 24-26, 10am-5pm. Adults £2.50,
children, OAPs and unemployed £1.50.

Museum of Transport
Kelvin Hall, 1 Bunhouse Road, Glasgow, G3 8DP
Tel: 0141 357 3929
A small collection of motorcycles including
Automobile Association BSA combination. Open
Mon-Sat 10am-5pm. Sunday 11am-5pm. Closed
December 25 and January 1. Admission free.

Myreton Motor Museum
Aberlady, Longniddry, East Lothian, EH32 0PZ
Tel: 018757 288
A small collection including 1926 350cc Chater-Lea
racer and Egli Vincent. Open Easter to Oct 10am-
5pm and Oct to Easter 10am-6pm. Closed Dec 25
and Jan 1. Adults £2, children 50p.

National Motor Museum
Brockenhurst, Beaulieu, SO42 7ZN
Tel: 01590 612123/612345
Important motorcycle collection. Reference and
photographic libraries. Open Easter to Sept 10am-
6pm, Oct to Easter 10am-5pm. Closed Dec 25. Adults
£6.75, OAPs/students £5.25, children £4.75 (includes
Museum, rides and drives, Monastic Life Exhibition
and entry to Palace House and grounds).

National Motorcycle Museum
Coventry Road, Bickenhill, Solihull, B92 0EJ
Tel: 01675 53311

Royal Museum of Scotland
Chambers Street, Edinburgh, EH1 1JF
Tel: 0131 225 7534
Small display of engines and complete machines
including the world's first 4 cylinder motorcycle,
an 1895 Holden. Open Mon to Sat 10am-5pm. Sun
2pm-5pm. Closed Dec 25, Jan 1. Admission free.

Sammy Miller Museum,
Gore Road, New Milton, BH25 6TF
Tel: 01425 619696
Sammy Miller is a living legend in the world of
motorcycle racing, and the museum was opened in
1983 by John Surtees. All bikes are in working order
and wherever possible are run in classic bike events.
At present there are 200 bikes in the Museum, many
extremely rare. New exhibits are being sought all
the time, with much of the restoration work being
carried out on the premises by Sammy Miller
himself. There are interesting artefacts and items of
memorabilia, including many cups and trophies won
by Sammy over the years. A typical motorcycle
workshop of 1925 has been reconstructed. Open
10.30am-4.30pm every day, April-Oct 10.30am-
4.30pm, Sats and Suns Nov-March. 15 miles west of
Southampton and 10 miles east of Bournemouth at
New Milton, Hants.

Science Museum
Exhibition Road, South Kensington, SW7 2DD
Tel: 0171 589 3456
Collection of engines and complete machines, with
cutaway BSA A10, Yamaha XS1100, 1940 500cc
BMW and 1969 Honda CB750. Mon-Sat 10am-6pm.
Sun 11am-6pm. Closed Dec 24-26. Adults £4, OAPs and
children £2.10, disabled free. Most Science Museum's
motorcycle collection is at Wroughton Airfield near
Swindon, Wilts. Tel: 0793 814466

Stanford Hall Motorcycle Museum
Stanford Hall, Lutterworth, LE17 6DH
Tel: 01788 860250
Older machines and racers. Open Sats, Suns,
Bank Holiday Mondays and following Tues, Easter
to Sept, 2.30pm-6pm. (12 noon-6pm when a special
event is taking place.). Admission to grounds:
Adults £1.60, children 70p. Museum: Adults 90p,
children 20p.

Page numbers in italic refer to the colour sections

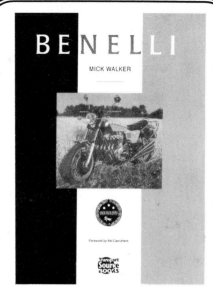
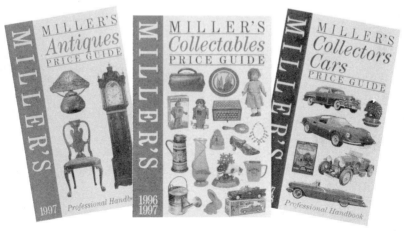